# The Art of Studying

# The Art of Studying

## A Guide for Student Nurses

EMMA SPANEY, PH.D.

*Associate Professor, Department of Psychology, Queens College; Consultant on Coordination, National League for Nursing; Formerly Assistant Director, Department of Measurement and Guidance, National League of Nursing Education; Associate in Foundations of Education, Teachers College, Columbia University*

AND

LOUISE A. JENNINGS, R.N., M.A.

*Lecturer, Nursing Science Program, Queens College; Formerly Instructor and Supervisor, Medical-Surgical Nursing, New Britain General Hospital, Connecticut.*

Illustrated by

Jean McConnell



J. B. LIPPINCOTT CO.

Philadelphia Montreal

Distributed in Great Britain by
Pitman Medical Publishing Co., Limited, London

Library of Congress Catalog Card No. 58-9283

Printed in the United States of America

Second Printing

# Contents

J.McC.

# 1

# Organizing for Action

Here you are, with one foot on the threshold of your chosen school of nursing! What will be expected of you? What kinds of experiences can you look forward to while you are a student? What can you do to help yourself meet these expectations fairly painlessly, while still getting as much satisfaction and enjoyment out of your experiences as possible? It is the purpose of the authors of this guide to make suggestions on ways to help you to become self-propelling in areas crucial to your academic success.

## WHAT WILL BE EXPECTED OF YOU?

To begin with, you probably expect certain things of yourself in relation to your behavior in the classroom, with patients and with your fellow-students. Probably you already have set certain standards of performance for yourself, based on your knowledge of your social and academic strengths and weaknesses. You will have an opportunity to become even better acquainted with yourself during the course of reading the following chapters.

Your instructors will expect certain things of

you in relation to fulfilling assignments, learning the vocabulary of nursing and measuring up to their standards for achievement. Especially at the beginning of your nursing-school experience, you can expect the classroom to loom large on your horizon.

As you progress beyond the "classroom" stage and spend increasing amounts of time on the wards with your clinical instructors, you will discover that patients, professional nurses and even doctors begin to expect things of you. They are seeing you as a nurse, even though *you* know you are still a student. The farther you progress toward the completion of your course, the greater will become the expectations which these people have of you.

## WHAT KINDS OF LEARNING EXPERIENCES ARE LIKELY TO BE OFFERED YOU?

If you will look at the printed materials which your school of nursing has provided, you probably will find a discussion of the objectives of the school. Most schools include this fairly close to the beginning in their catalogues, and although the specific words which will be used might differ somewhat, there is present an underlying theme —that of helping you to become a useful and productive member of society by assisting you to develop professional skills in nursing and social skills as a citizen and an individual. To these ends, the school has planned curricular activities, including formal class instruction, ward experiences with patients and visits to places of professional interest to potential nurses.

In addition to these curricular activities, which are aimed largely at professional goals, you will find clubs and other social activities which are designed to help you meet and work with as well as play with others successfully. Then, too, you may be entering a school in which two students are assigned to room together; this will give you an opportunity to learn to live with someone of your own age and approximate interests, if you have not already learned to do so. Becoming self-sufficient and being responsible for your own room and maintenance will also help you to get ready for the time when you will be on your own as a professional nurse in the community of your choice. It should be evident that learning experiences will exist not only in the classroom and ward situations but also with friends and companions as you work and play together.

## WHAT KINDS OF PERFORMANCE TASKS ARE LIKELY TO BE REQUIRED OF YOU AS EVIDENCES OF LEARNING?

First, probably, will be the task of reading and assimilating textbook materials and then that of being able to answer questions in class about what you have read. After that, there is the ever-present job of passing both written and performance tests. Probably you already have taken a battery of tests prior to admission to the school of nursing, so you have had some experience with so-called "objective" tests. This is the form in which your licensing examinations will be presented. In addition to these objective tests prepared by a professional test-making agency, you will have teacher-made tests of either the objective or the essay type to cope with. So far, we have mentioned only paper-and-pencil tests. However, there are some kinds of skills which cannot be tested adequately in this way. For example, the way in which you approach a new patient can be tested best by watching what you do and say in such a situation—how you prepare to meet him by finding out all you can about him ahead of time, what you say to him, how you handle his responses to you, etc.

Probably you will have to write reports of at least two types: the type that is based on bibliographic sources, which will require library skills, and the nursing care report based on your observation and care of patients.

## HOW CAN YOU GET MAXIMUM RETURNS FOR THE TIME YOU WILL INVEST IN YOUR NURSING COURSE?

The rest of this guide is devoted to suggestions in areas where students have previously asked for help. These suggestions are based on what psychologists and other behavioral scientists have discovered about how people learn and remember, what makes them tick and why and how much the individual who is seriously motivated to learn can do for himself.

Your school of nursing has planned its curriculum to help you become the kind of nurse who can meet the expectations of patients, their families, other nurses, members of allied professions and doctors, to mention only a few. Probably at this point you are wondering how this can be done and still leave the potential nurse time for relaxation and play! However, remember that quite a number of others have succeeded in becoming good nurses. How did they do it? Are there "tricks of the trade" which can make even the beginning classroom experiences with their heavy academic load relatively painless? The answer is "YES!"

The following areas are discussed in subsequent pages:

Planning your study corner
Budgeting your time
Becoming a more efficient reader
Becoming a more efficient note-taker
Becoming a more efficient test-taker
Improving arithmetic skills
Improving observational skills
Writing nursing care reports
Writing reports based on library sources

We hope that your excursion through these topics will be both profitable and enjoyable, and that you will want to return to some of our suggestions in the future for a second and perhaps even a third consideration. However, a word of caution is in order. Don't expect to change your habits over night. After all, you have had them for several years! Be patient with yourself. Don't set your sights too high at first and keep tabs on your progress. If you stay with it, you may turn out to be a pleasant surprise to yourself!

J. McConnell

# 2

# Planning Your Study Corner

Educational psychologists tell us that it is desirable to have a definite place set aside for studying, furnished as effectively and attractively as possible. The reason for this is fairly obvious. Efficient study habits do not come naturally to most of us but must be learned consciously. The less we have to fight ourselves to form them, the less frustration we have to cope with in reaching our goal. We might begin by considering how much space you have available for your study. Have you a separate room which can be devoted to this important activity, or will you have a "study corner" in some section of your room?

## LOCATING YOUR STUDY CORNER

Are you rooming alone—having only your own wishes to consult, or must you consider the placement of your roommate's study corner as well? Since you will be spending a considerable amount of your out-of-class time studying, you should devote to it as pleasant a corner or section of the room, in terms of lighting and ventilation, as possible. Remember the importance of taking care of your body if you want it to stay awake and work at top efficiency! If possible, the location should be such that you can leave your well-organized confusion on top of the desk or table, secure in the knowledge that it will remain untouched by human hands should you interrupt study for an hour or two of other activities. However, take note of local regulations—many dormitories and nurse's residences require that rooms be organized for the periodic rounds of cleaning personnel.

## FURNISHING YOUR STUDY CORNER

### Essentials

First you will need a chair and a desk or a table on which all major activities will take place. Next, it is a good idea to have on the desk-top a shelf, a chest or a box for books and papers not in immediate use, keeping there only what you will need for a particular stint. Since, on occasion, you undoubtedly will be working after dark, a desk-lamp is desirable if there are no floor-lamps that can be shifted around for study purposes.

You will need some kind of container—tray, jar or box—for your pens, pencils, ruler, eraser, etc. In this day of easy-to-use ball-point pens, it is well to remember the relative advantages and disadvantages of the pen versus the pencil in your work. This is largely a matter of your own note-taking habits. If you prefer a pencil, it is a good idea to use a mechanical one in order to save precious minutes, rather than one you have to be forever sharpening. If your mechanical pencil needs to be uncapped before the eraser can be used, you will find that an eraser fitted over the outside will be a time-saver. If this is not possible, then a pencil-type eraser is the next best bet. It is a good idea also to have a pen and a pencil solely for use in the study corner and another set which can be clipped into your notebook or carried in your purse, for class use. It is surprising how much time can be lost in looking for mislaid pens and pencils, in sharpening dull points and in getting at coyly hidden erasers!

Many students have found it helpful to include an alarm clock as a study corner accessory, preferably one with a gently nudging voice rather than a shriek to raise the dead. (You may need the latter to awaken you in the morning, in which case keep this type on your bedside table.) If the alarm is set for half-hourly or hourly intervals during a period of study time, you can pace yourself in terms of what your time-budget calls for (see next chapter). This is especially helpful when you are trying to get a lot of pesky little things done in a relatively short time, or when you know that the time-allowance is inadequate, and you want to push yourself to increase your pace.

**Providing the "Study-Lures"**

The next considerations are those of making the study corner attractive to you, personally, in so far as this is humanly possible. This may be done in several ways: by the use of colorful pens, pencils, ruler, desk-blotter, chair-cushion and alarm clock; by placing an attractive picture or poster where you can lift your eyes from your books and see it across the room (this will provide needed rest for your eyes during reading bouts—see chapter on "Becoming a More Efficient

Reader"); and by attractive arrangement of book-ends; favorite gadgets for paper-weights; etc., but do keep it to essentials.

Then there are the little problems of "drinks" and "starvation," both of which have a way of assailing us in the midst of serious study. You may find it advantageous to keep a thermos flask of plain water, milk or fruit juice on your desk, and gum and/or hard candy within easy reach as well. Although it is socially a dubious habit in our culture to chew gum in the company of others, you may find it tension-relieving when you are alone. If you become conscious of that "all gone" feeling of hunger long before it is time to stop, one or two hard candies may satisfy your need without the mess or the loss of time which more extensive feeding would entail. However, if in the midst of your study-periods you find yourself getting hunger pangs, you might consider your calorie count for the day and the possibility of taking a piece of fruit at this time.

If you room alone, you have the alternative of facing your desk to the wall or into the room. Your choice depends on your knowledge of your own work habits. By sitting down at your desk you are telling yourself that you mean business now—full steam ahead! Some people settle down more quickly with their backs to the room, facing the wall, while others find that they work better facing the other way. If you have no strong feelings to begin with, experiment until you find the most attractive position *for you*.

If you have a roommate, these same considerations will apply, but the solution will depend on how large your room is and the type of available space. Usually it is not a good idea to place the two desks together, face-to-face. On the contrary, you both may find it advantageous to face to the wall in order to respect each other's study-time privacy as much as possible.

### Informing Others "Student at Work"

Although it may be possible for you and your friends to arrange your time-budgets in such a way as to have the same periods of time set aside for studying, many students have found it profitable to inform would-be callers of their study activities by means of various "Do not disturb" signs. Among these you might wish to consider the idea of a clockface with movable hands to indicate the end of your study period, combined with the posting of a "Studying Science" or "Studying for a Test" sign, etc. This is helpful to those who would a-calling go, too, because they know at what time they can reasonably expect to get your (relatively) undivided attention. Of course, the foundation of a good system of signals rests on a gentlemen's agreement with your roommate that once either of you is seated at her desk, she is not to be disturbed except for good cause. If your roommate is studying and you are reading for pleasure or doing other nonstudy tasks in your room, it is considerate to answer knocks on the door and to explain the situation, thus helping your roommate to keep her study time intact. She can protect you in the same way if the situation is reversed. But before you do this, talk it over with her to be sure she agrees with these ideas!

One last suggestion—although a radio is a very wonderful and attractive instrument, place it as far away from your study corner as possible. Most people find that they can concentrate better for those "long hauls" when there is as little interference as possible.

TIME BUDGET

# 3

# Budgeting Your Time

Although it is an accepted notion that there are 24 hours in an Earth day, you may find that there are so many things to get done that you feel like a whirling dervish and wish that you could stop the mad whirl! Classes, studying, social activities, studying, household tasks, studying, eating, sleeping, studying . . . studying. . . .

Efficient study habits are a "must" if you are to have any time for social activities and for just plain putting your feet up and doing nothing.

## HAVE YOU DISCOVERED THE ADVANTAGES OF A TIME-BUDGET?

Keeping a time-budget is very much like keeping a money-budget—you know how much you have to spend, and you allocate money to cover the essentials or "musts" first, then "wants" and finally, if any is left, "surplus" or "fun-fund" or what you will. If during the week, month or whatever time-period is covered, you decide to reallocate funds, you do so in full awareness that you will have to do some juggling, since the total sum of money to be allocated remains the same. Time-budgets work in exactly the same way.

If you already are keeping a time-budget, the following discussion may give you some additional ideas. If you don't know how to keep a time-budget but let every day take care of itself, you may end up having to burn the midnight oil to get your "musts" done, to the detriment of your health and well-being.

## WHEN TO DO WHAT?

Most of the people who keep a time-budget find a weekly one more profitable than a daily one. This will make good sense in your situation, since you will receive a weekly class-schedule. There are at least three basic kinds of time-needs to be considered: (1) time for those things which *have* to be done, (2) time for those things it would be *nice* to do and (3) "safety-valve" time. This last is like a "miscellaneous" envelope in a money-budget or an "emergency fund" and is to be used to help get the "musts" done *only if necessary*. Otherwise, blissful thought, it is yours to spend in any way you like—perhaps working ahead to make next week's "musts" lighter, perhaps just to sit and ruminate!

### "Musts"

Among the "musts" usually included are items like class attendance; class readings and assignments; clothes; grooming; personal hygiene needs; room maintenance; religious observances; eating; sleeping; letters to parents, family and friends, etc. Although you probably will be making new friends at school, it is nevertheless important to remember the value of keeping up good family and other social relationships against the time when you will be graduated and perhaps return to your home community to work and/or play during the holiday times.

### "Wants"

Among the "wants" usually included are items like participation in club programs, social and recreational activities, etc.

## WHAT DO YOU KNOW ABOUT YOURSELF?

Before we can go on, you will have to ask yourself some pertinent questions. Are you the kind of person who studies well at night, or do you fall asleep over your books? Maybe you would do better to get up at 5 or 6 A.M. and study before the day's events crowd into your consciousness. If you want to try this on yourself, perform only the minimally necessary hygienic measures when you get up, staying in your robe, and then settle right down to studying. Set the alarm for the time when you would ordinarily arise, and when it rings, dress and perform the rest of your morning ritual at that time. In this way the things which you have been studying can be "mulled over" while you prepare yourself for the fray.

What about the rapidity with which you can get yourself into a "studying mood"? After a hard day, do you need to get used to the idea of studying? Most of us do better if we take a little time to get comfortable and to "run down" after being "wound up" all day. If you are physically tired, a few minutes with your shoes off and your feet up before tackling the next task may be a good idea. Also, you may need a lift in the way of food; a piece of fruit, candy, or other small snack may do the trick. Some people have found gum-chewing a relaxing activity in this situation, although, once again, it should be recognized that this is sometimes restricted in our culture to the privacy of one's own castle!

You may wish to read some form of "light" literature for a short time—romance, murder mystery, science fiction or whatever appeals to you. Sometimes a few household tasks provide welcome activity after sitting in class for several hours. Whatever it is, you should choose something which will help you to make the transition to studying less painful. However, it is a good idea either to set your alarm or to cue yourself in some other way for the end of your "mood" period in order not to use up all your available time in getting ready to study, with none being left for the actual task!

Once again we are ready to consider the specifics of your time-budget. One thing to keep constantly in mind is that there is nothing sacred about it—it should not rule you—it is only a guide to be altered as the need arises, and *you* are the one who makes the decisions! For example, if you just simply can't stand studying another minute, and the budget calls for another hour of it, change your activity and come back to the task when you think you can again profit from your expenditure of time. Adjust your future budget accordingly. You will have to do some juggling around, to be sure, but if you leave some unallotted time each day as a safety-valve and confine your planned study activities to 6 days in the week as well, this should be entirely possible.

## SOME MECHANICS OF TIME BUDGETING

Like most of our personal routines, the keeping of a time-budget is a highly individual thing, and no one can devise a scheme which is equally good for all. Therefore, the following procedure should be considered merely suggestive. If you like it exactly as it is, that's fine, but don't hesitate to experiment with your own ideas.

Some students have found it helpful to use a piece of 8½ inch by 11 inch paper (notebook size will do, too) divided into 7 columns, one for each day in the week. Then divide the page in half horizontally. Use the upper half of the page to list specifically what you must do each day in order to meet your class assignments, etc., and those things you would like to do each day in the way of club meetings and other activities. Use the lower half to plan when you will do these things, day by day. You might block this out in hourly or half-hourly intervals, starting with the time you get up and ending with the time you go to bed. Enter your class attendance time for each day, your "mood" time and your "safety-valve" time. You know best how many hours of sleep you need. However, if this is more than 8 hours a day as a rule, you had better consult your health advisor; you may be in need of a dietary change to give you more energy-building foods.

Now look at the time left each day. This is for study and for the remaining "musts" as well as the "likes." At the beginning, there may be little time left for the "likes." However, if you adapt to your needs the technics suggested in the following pages of this guide, you should be able to remedy this situation before very long. Remember that this is only suggestive!

### DO YOU NEED A DAY-STRETCHER?

Now that you have had a try at making your weekly time-budget, do you feel that you need a day-stretcher? If so, answer the following questions by placing an "X" over either "Yes" or "No" to help you pinpoint some of the areas where you need to take hold in order to use your available time more effectively.

| | |
|---|---|
| 1. Do you wish that you could read faster? | 1. Yes No |
| 2. Do you wish that you understood better what you read? | 2. Yes No |
| 3. Do you need a conducted tour through your class notes when you try to study for a test because they lack organization? | 3. Yes No |
| 4. Do you have difficulty in taking notes from your text without almost copying the text over? | 4. Yes No |
| 5. Does your mind "go blank" in an examination? | 5. Yes No |
| 6. In answering essay questions, do you "run dry" after a sentence or two? or Do you keep repeating the same one or two ideas over and over? | 6. Yes No |
| 7. Do you have trouble with arithmetical processes? | 7. Yes No |
| 8. Do you have trouble writing down briefly and accurately what you observe with your sensory organs? | 8. Yes No |
| 9. Do you waste time in the library because you don't know how to find pertinent material? | 9. Yes No |
| 10. Do you have to rewrite your reading notes before making a rough draft of a report or written paper? | 10. Yes No |

The guide below will suggest the most helpful chapters for you to consult in terms of the questions to which you answered "Yes."

| If you answered Yes to Question | refer to Chapter |
|---|---|
| 1, 2 | 4. Becoming a More Efficient Reader |
| 3, 4 | 5. Becoming a More Efficient Note-Taker |
| 5, 6 | 6. Becoming a More Efficient Test-Taker |
| 7 | 7. Improving Arithmetic Skills |
| 8 | 8. Improving Observational Skills |
| 9, 10 | 10. Writing Reports Based on Library Sources |

# 4

# Becoming a More Efficient Reader

Undoubtedly you have been reading several different kinds of printed materials for a number of years. However, it is probably also true that you have not given much thought to the actual process of reading since early elementary school years, when your teachers tried to help you read accurately, rapidly and understandingly.

## WHAT IS INVOLVED IN READING?

The two aspects of the reading process which we shall consider are *rate,* or the rapidity with which you read, and *comprehension,* or the degree to which you understand what you have read.

In order to continue with this chapter, you will need a stop watch or a watch with a sweep second hand, so that you can time yourself in minutes and seconds. When you have located your timing device, record your starting time and begin to read at the asterisk below, and stop when you reach the second asterisk.

*Enter Your Starting Time Here* 7:15.

* Detailed studies of the eye-movements of both fast and slow readers have been made and form the foundation for our knowledge about reading rate. Both the numbers of eye-fixations and the patterns of these fixations showed differences not only from one individual to another but also for the same individual when different kinds of printed materials were used. The eyes of rapid readers fixate in the middle of the line, if the span is sufficiently short for them, or twice on a line if the span is longer. They seldom go back over what they have read on a line. On the other hand, the eyes of slow readers fixate on every word and have many more "goings back" or regressions, as they are technically termed. This business of eye-span is an individual thing and differs from one person to another. Some publishers have tried to help their readers by using double-columns in their books, thus shortening the length of a reading line.

One of the things which may be operating to slow down your reading rate is the habit of "mouthing" words, that is, forming them with your lips as you read. If you do this, then obviously you fixate your eyes on every word and possibly even more than once on a word, if it is strange or unduly long. In this same category is the "subvocalizer," the person who says the words to himself "in his throat" but does not move his lips. These habits can be detected fairly easily by placing the tips of your fingers lightly over your mouth, if you suspect "mouthing," or by placing your left thumb under your left ear and curling your left hand *lightly* around your throat so that the index finger is under the right ear, if you suspect "subvocalization." In this case, you will be able to feel the vibration of the throat.

The question of what makes some people understand better than others what they have read is not a simple one to answer. To say that the differences lie basically in the richness of previous background and experience as a frame of reference for what is currently being read is probably correct, without being very helpful! Certainly the extensiveness of the reader's vocabulary is one consideration here. However, it is all too true that a good, all-around vocabulary will not be particularly helpful for reading material in a technical specialty. For example, your knowledge of the meaning of words like "exculpate" and "amanuensis" will not help very much in reading a textbook on anatomy and physiology.

Although some immediate word-recognition might be involved (after all, words like "and," "the" and "but" are still the same), of greater importance is the ability to get the meaning of words in context, that is, in the word-setting in which they are being used. For example, you certainly know the word "run"—or do you? Does it mean "run home because it's raining," or "run for office in a club," or "run in my stocking," or "run him down on a busy street"? Actually, the word "run" out of context can have many meanings, and you need additional cues in the form of companion words before you know which one of these meanings to select. Now, actually, we don't go through a questioning procedure with ourselves in such a lengthy way when we come upon "run" in our reading. It's as though our mental dispatcher telegraphs ahead in terms of the words we read before we get to "run," so that the proper switch is thrown when we get there, and we are mentally shunted onto a line leading to the correct meaning for this situation.

It is helpful, too, to be able to "reason out" strange or unfamiliar words. This requires a knowledge of word-anatomy and of how to dissect words; it makes prefixes, suffixes, combining forms and what might be called "root" words very important. If you have studied languages, especially Latin and Greek, you will find this useful now, since many of the words in your technical nursing vocabulary are derived from Latin and Greek sources. However, even here it is possible to pull boners! Take, for example, the *pediatric* nurse. The Latin student might infer very happily that *ped* comes from the Latin *pes* meaning "foot" and conclude that this nurse specializes in foot disorders, whereas actually it comes from the Greek *paes* meaning "child," and she really specializes in caring for children. The moral of this story is that it is a good idea to check "reasoning out" with a dictionary whenever this is possible. However, as you continue to do this, you will build more confidence in yourself and a better background for future reasoning out, so that you will not be completely helpless in the face of technical material even when no dictionary is available.*

*Enter Stopping Time Here* ....7:17 50....

*Time To Read Passage* ....2.... minutes ....50.... seconds.

Now consider the following statements *without going back over the reading passage*. Mark "X" over the letter "T" if the statement is true according to the material marked off between the asterisks, and over the letter "F" if it is false. Mark "CT" if you can't tell *from the reading passage* whether it is true or false.

1. A study of the eye-movements of rapid readers shows that they have no regressions — 1. T F CT
2. "Mouthing" is the same as "subvocalizing." — 2. T F CT
3. Although "mouthing" can be detected, it cannot be cured. — 3. T F CT
4. The extensiveness of the reader's vocabulary is an important consideration in his ability to comprehend what he has read. — 4. T F CT
5. There is some immediate word-recognition involved in most of our reading. — 5. T F CT
6. Words need to be considered in context, especially if they have more than one possible meaning. — 6. T F CT
7. The more foreign languages you know, the better able you will be to understand technical literature. — 7. T F CT
8. One should never accept the results of "reasoning out" unfamiliar words without checking in a dictionary. — 8. T F CT
9. An English word may sometimes appear to have come from two different sources. — 9. T F CT
10. If a person tries to force himself to read faster in order to improve his rate, he may suffer a decline in comprehension. — 10. T F CT

You will find the correct answers indicated at the end of this chapter under "WHAT IS INVOLVED IN READING?"

*Enter Your Score Here* .........7.........

## HOW WELL DO YOU READ?

The starred reading passage which you have just completed has approximately 800 words. Calculate your reading time in minutes and seconds. Then use the table below to help you get your approximate reading rate for the passage.

| If your time was | Your approximate number of words per minute is |
|---|---|
| 8 minutes | 100 words |
| 7 minutes | 115 words |
| 6 minutes | 135 words |
| 5 minutes | 160 words |
| 4 minutes | 200 words |
| 3½ minutes | 230 words |
| 3 minutes | 270 words |
| 2½ minutes | 320 words |
| 2 minutes | 400 words |
| 1½ minutes | 530 words |
| 1 minute | 800 words |

If you are reading at the rate of 500 words per minute or better, *and* if your comprehension score is 9 or 10, you are doing very well so far as simple expository reading is concerned.

You may be able to get additional information about your reading speed and level of comprehension from your Guidance Counselor if your school has one, or from your Educational Director. Probably you took a standardized reading test as one of the battery of tests administered prior to your admission to the school of nursing.

If you did, the results probably are reported in terms of your percentile rank with regard to applicants to basic diploma programs. For example, if your reading speed is at the 75th percentile and your comprehension is at the 90th percentile with regard to such applicants, it means that your reading speed score equals or exceeds that of 75 per cent of these applicants, while your comprehension score equals or exceeds that of 90 per cent of these applicants.

### CHOOSING TECHNICS TO SUIT PURPOSE

The choice of a particular reading technic is like choosing a dress. This involves a consideration of the purpose (for what type of occasion are you dressing?), what is available, and therefore what will give the best results. The reader who has a single set of technics for all types of materials is like the girl who thinks that she can wear a suit on every social occasion.

The experienced reader does not tackle light reading for pleasure armed with vocabulary cards, pencil and dictionary; nor expect to profit from reading a science textbook in bed with the radio playing! In the same way, you should not expect to skip as lightly over technical text materials as you do over materials which are written mostly "in English." No discussion of the need for changing technics to suit the purpose would be complete without Sir Francis Bacon's famous remark on the subject, "Some books are to be tasted, others to be swallowed, and some few to be chewed and digested."

### READING MORE TECHNICAL MATERIAL

Now try yourself on the following passage, which is illustrative of the science materials with which you will be coping. Record your starting time and begin to read at the first asterisk and stop at the second.

*Enter Your Starting Time Here* ..................

* When the kidney is examined microscopically, it is seen to be composed of structures resembling tiny funnels, with long, convoluted stems. The upper portions of these structures are called Bowman's capsules. In each of these capsules is a cluster of capillaries, called a glomerulus. The Bowman's capsules and the enclosed glomerulus are called renal corpuscles. A tubule with a convoluted portion extends from each Bowman's capsule. A renal corpuscle and the above-mentioned tubule together constitute a nephron. The renal corpuscle and the convoluted tubule are active in the formation of urine. The function of the straight tubule is to collect urine after it is formed.

Normally, the kidneys perform four functions. These are: (1) to excrete certain harmful waste products from the blood; (2) to excrete certain beneficial substances from the blood, when they are present in excessive amounts; (3) to help regulate the blood volume and osmotic pressure by excreting excessive amounts of water and (4) to help maintain a normal proportion of electrolytes in the blood, thereby assisting in the maintenance of the acid-base balance.

The first step in urine formation is filtration. This takes place in the renal corpuscles. The second step is reabsorption, which takes place in the tubules. The structural differences of cells which comprise these two kidney units account for the difference in function. The capsule cell is thin and flat, resembling the cells of the alveoli of the lungs; the tubule cells are thick and columnar, more like epithelial cells.

The cells of the tubules possess a high degree of selectivity. Normally, the tubule cells absorb all glucose; however, when glucose is present in the blood in excessive amounts (more than 170 to 180 mg. per cc. of blood), the cells apparently are unable to reabsorb the entire amount, and the excess is excreted in the urine. This is what happens in diabetes mellitus.

An important ability of the kidney, and one which seems to be lost very early in some kidney diseases, is the ability to concentrate urine, which is determined by measuring its specific gravity. Normally, the kidney excretes a given amount of solids per unit of fluid. The normal specific gravity is 1.017. Many conditions influence the concentration of urine. If the climate is cold, if fluid is not being lost by other channels of excretion (lungs, skin), then the amount of fluid being eliminated by the kidneys may be high, but the amount of solids is not affected. The specific gravity may be as low as 1.002. On the other hand, if the climate is very warm, if the body is losing fluids by sweating, vomiting, or diarrhea, then the kidney attempts to protect the body from more fluid loss by excreting small amounts of fluid. The specific gravity may become very high, 1.030 or more.

The ability of the kidney to concentrate may be tested by limiting fluid intake and collecting urine specimens at regular intervals. The specific gravity of the specimens is measured, and a picture of the concentrating powers of the kidney is obtained.*

*Enter Your Stopping Time Here* ..............

*Total Time For Reading Passage* .............. min. .............. sec.

Now consider the following statements *without going back over the reading passage*. Place an X over the letter "T" if the statement is true according to the passage, over "F" if it is false and over "CT" if you can't tell from reading the passage whether it is true or false.

| | | |
|---|---|---|
| 1. The glomerulus is encased in Bowman's capsule. | 1. T F CT |
| 2. A nephron is made up of a renal corpuscle and a tubule. | 2. T F CT |
| 3. The straight tubule is active in the formation of urine. | 3. T F CT |
| 4. Renal concentration is dependent upon the adequacy of peripheral circulation. | 4. T F CT |
| 5. There are 5 functions which the kidneys normally perform. | 5. T F CT |
| 6. The cells of the capsule resemble the cells of the alveoli of the lungs. | 6. T F CT |
| 7. Filtration takes place in the kidney tubules. | 7. T F CT |
| 8. The normal specific gravity of urine is 1.030. | 8. T F CT |
| 9. Climate has no effect upon the amount of urine excreted. | 9. T F CT |
| 10. In diabetes mellitus the ability of the kidney to concentrate is affected. | 10. T F CT |

You will find the correct answers indicated at the end of the chapter under "READING MORE TECHNICAL MATERIAL." The reading passage contains approximately 500 words. If you are reading more than 275 words per minute *and* your comprehension score is 9 or 10, you are doing well.

It is possible that, even though you have turned in a creditable performance, you may wish to do even better. If so, the rest of this chapter is devoted to suggestions for the improvement of both rate and comprehension.

## IMPROVING READING RATE

Most students find that 3 hours of concentrated reading for factual information is about all they can take before that famous "law of diminishing returns" sets in. Therefore, it behooves you to get as great a return per unit of time expended as is possible. Of course, the physical aids are quite important: have your eyes checked regularly; see that you have good lighting and ventilation; rest your eyes at intervals (half-hourly or so) by looking into the distance—perhaps at that favorite picture or poster mentioned in Chapter 2: Planning Your Study Corner.

### Push Yourself Against Time

If you earnestly desire to speed up your reading rate, you must force yourself to take in (and comprehend) more words at a glance. It is a good idea to start with fiction or some other light reading and try to fixate your eyes no more than twice on a line. Don't force yourself to keep this up for more than 15 minutes daily. One way of doing this is to set the alarm to go off in 15 minutes and then settle down to your light reading. The first day, don't try to speed, just read as you are accustomed to doing, and record the number of pages read. Then the second day begin to speed up, again recording the number of pages. Remember that comprehension is important, too, so don't push yourself too fast. As you gain speed after 10 days or so of doing this, set yourself a certain number of pages to do the next time before the alarm goes off, based on your current reading rate. For example, if you have been reading 20 pages in your 15-minute interval, try to set 21 as your goal and see how many reading periods it takes you to reach this; then try 22, etc.

By forcing yourself to read against time, you are making yourself take in groups of words rather than single words and then larger and larger groups, until you may reach the point where a quick look at the middle of the line will enable you to get the sense of the entire line.

### Concentration

In order to embark on a self-improvement program of the type under discussion, or indeed in order to be able to get maximum reading return per unit of time expended in any field, you must be able to concentrate, that is, to give undivided attention to the task before you. This can be helped by your having a place for study (study corner) and a time for study (time budget). However, you also need a device for ridding yourself of interfering thoughts and notions. For example, you may be going along swimmingly on your speed-up reading program, only to hit the word "artifact." This reminds you (because of the "art" no doubt) that you saw a very fine illustrative diagram in an anatomy book that you were examining in the library this morning and forgot to go back and get. Now, unless we set up a method whereby you can *then and there* make a note to remind yourself to do something about this diagram, you may as well stop trying to push yourself to read faster for this session, because the diagram probably will keep popping up to plague you, no matter how hard you may try to keep it down.

For this reason, it is a good idea to keep a small pad and pencil handy so that you can record any vagrant pearls of wisdom which occur to you and which might otherwise prevent your concentrating further on the task at hand. Once these pearls have been preserved for later consideration, you should have no further difficulty. (If you awaken in the middle of the night with a bright idea or a nagging thought which must be pursued the next day, you'll find that a bedside pad and pencil on which you can jot it down will help you to get back to sleep more quickly.)

### Publications and Mechanical Devices

If you feel that you need more help in speeding up your reading rate than you can get from the kind of analysis presented here, you should talk with your Guidance Counselor or Educational Director. It may be possible for you to enroll in a reading improvement class. If not, some very helpful books are available on how to speed up, together with reading passages graded in difficulty which are designed to be read against time. See whether or not your school library has any of these reading aids, by looking in the card catalogue under "Reading Improvement."

Also available for self-help are mechanical gadgets based on the idea of varying the rate at which reading material is presented. If your school does not have any of these publications or mechanical devices, a letter to the Department of Education of your local college or teacher-education institution will bring you suggestions about the most recent self-helps. Your school librarian might be able to arrange for you to get these on an inter-library loan.

## IMPROVING COMPREHENSION

Most students who embark on a speed-up program fear serious loss of comprehension as a consequence and are pleasantly surprised to find that it does not occur. As one student put it, "It's not only that I understand just as much, but I can do it almost twice as fast!" We shall not be satisfied with merely holding our own, but rather shall look forward to the further extension of our comprehension skills.

### Extending Your Vocabulary

Most of us probably would consider a dictionary part of our necessary equipment for reading an article in a foreign language. However, if it is written in English, which is our mother tongue, then surely we ought to be able to get along on what we have! So perhaps we might not be able to give a really concise definition of 1 or 2 (or 3) words in the article, but we get the *sense* of the thing—we can tell what it's all about! While this may have been enough in the past, the kind of reading which you will meet in your technical courses will require you to know a little more than just a vague idea of what the author had in mind. Precise definitions will be called for, and a considerable number of technical words will appear. Although these materials will be printed "in English," you will need a good dictionary at hand in order to understand what is going on.

### Keeping a Word-File

Many students have found it helpful to keep a word-file handy when they do technical reading. This may be done by using a 3 inch by 5 inch file card for each new word and keeping the cards filed behind alphabetical dividers. There are inexpensive cardboard or plastic boxes available to hold these cards, and the system has the advantage of being flexible enough to permit new words to be added to new cards and new meanings for words already in the file to be added to the appropriate cards.

For ease in filing, one way of setting up the card is to print the word in the upper right-hand corner. Then, if you can dissect it, record next the combining form or prefix with its meaning and/or the suffix with its meaning. Draw a line under this to show that it is by way of explanation. Then give the definitions for the word, numbering them as you go. It's a good idea, too, to use a colored pencil for noting illustrative uses of the word or any other points you may wish to

```
                              ENTERORRHAPHY

entero (G) — intestine

-rrhaphy (G) — suture of
-----------------------------------------
1. act of sewing up gap in intestine
```

record. You will find a list of combining forms, prefixes and suffixes in Appendix A in the back of this book.

For example, suppose you come across the word *enterorrhaphy* in your reading. Upon consulting the Appendix, a card might be made out like the one on the previous page.

### Assimilating New Words

One of the main problems in learning scientific vocabulary is the process by which it becomes part of the operational equipment of the reader. Because they try to assimilate too large a number of new words at one sitting, most students find this memorization process painful, like bolting too large an amount of food at one time. A far less painful and more rewarding technic for remembering these words is to go over the cards as frequently as possible, even if only short periods of time are available. As one student remarked, "It's a lot like picking up your knitting." In those few minutes while you wait for your roommate to go to breakfast, or while you wait for the class to begin, or even while you ride on a bus or a train, take out your vocabulary cards and read through them, making an effort on the third or fourth time around to anticipate the definition before you read it. You will find that running through these cards a few times during the day will help to fix the definitions in your memory less painfully than will a long-drawn-out memorization session. Also, if you say the word and its definition out loud as you read, you will find that this will help you to fix it in your memory because you are being doubly stimulated—through your eyes as you read and through your ears as you speak. Of course, you should be careful where you do this, lest you be suspected of "talking to yourself."

As you follow this procedure, you will find that your knowledge of word-anatomy is growing and that your hunches about the meanings of new words are being increasingly borne out by what your check-up in the dictionary reveals. You are getting experience in a method of handling word-problems which will make you more self-sufficient in your reading. This is especially important if you plan to continue your academic preparation for your profession beyond the basic program.

### Improving Your Frame of Reference

You are probably reading this book either because the idea of studying stimulated you (if anyone has anything to say on this subject, you want to know about it), or the "for nurses" in the title caught your eye (since you are a potential nurse, anything for nurses is for you), or both. Now, you may have specific study problems; or you may feel that the whole area of studying needs a good overhauling. On the other hand, you may be very happy with the study habits you have but want to see what this book is all about just out of intellectual curiosity.

"Studying" covers a large area. Did you try to make this more specific for yourself before you began to read? If you have a specific study problem, did you look to see whether or not it was discussed in this book, and if so, where and how? Usually you can improve the frame of reference within which you read a particular author's work by using a sequence somewhat as follows: (1) read the table of contents to get an idea of the scope of the coverage, the sequence of topics and the location within the sequence of topics of particular interest to you; (2) if there is a summary chapter at the end of the book (some may have it at the beginning), read this next to get a brief idea of what is going on in the author's frame of reference and (3) next tackle the chapters, first reading the chapter summary if there is one, then glancing over section headings within the chapter if these are present, and finally reading the material in each paragraph. For example, in this book, we have followed the practice of centering main headings, and locating subheadings beginning at the left margin in bold-face type. You may wish to reread the summary chapter at the completion of your chapter readings, in order to clinch your understanding of the author's point of view, the extent of his coverage, or both.

As you read each paragraph, try to keep the main idea in mind. Separate it from the illustrations, expansions of the main idea, etc. How does it relate to the framework you have obtained from the foregoing procedure? What do you think ought to come next in the development? How do you feel about what you are reading? We might propose the key words:

SELECT RELATE
ANTICIPATE EVALUATE

Also, you frequently will find helps in the format of what you are reading: numbers, or points being enumerated; contrast words like "on the one hand," or "on the other hand," etc.; reference words like "latter," "former," "given above," etc.; the type face, as for example, **bold face** or *italics*.

### Note-Taking for Future Reference

Of course, if you are reading for factual information, and wish to have a record of your readings with which to refresh your memory at a later date, it is necessary to take reading notes. You will find some suggestions for note-taking in the next chapter.

## CORRECT ANSWERS

### What Is Involved in Reading?

| | |
|---|---|
| 1. F | 6. T |
| 2. F | 7. CT |
| 3. CT | 8. F |
| 4. T | 9. T |
| 5. T | 10. CT |

### Reading More Technical Material

| | |
|---|---|
| 1. T | 6. T |
| 2. T | 7. F |
| 3. F | 8. F |
| 4. CT | 9. F |
| 5. F | 10. T |

KNOWLEDGE
FACT
FACT
FACT
FACT
FACT
FACT
NOTE BOOK
NOTE BOOK
FACT
FACT
FACT
FACT
FACT
J.McC.

# 5

# Becoming a More Efficient Note-Taker

When you sit down in your study corner or in the library to read for factual information, which one of these students is most like you—the one who feels that every printed word is precious, that the author knows so much more about the subject than the reader does (and who therefore copies down practically every word); or the student who takes no notes until the entire book is read and then finds precious little to write down? Actually, there is a perfectly common-sense approach to this question of what kind of reading notes to take. You take the kind that will do you the most good, that is, will be the most helpful to you in terms of the purpose for which you are reading.

## READING TO "LEARN THE TEXT"

First let us consider the reading of assigned pages in a textbook as preparation for a class session. The task is to condense the text to permit main ideas to be reproduced on demand, as, for example, in a class recitation, a quiz or a formal examination.

### Establishing a Frame of Reference

What relationship does reading of the text have to class lectures? Do you "read ahead" of the instructor, before the material is covered in class, or do you "read behind" the instructor? If you do the latter, then your class notes should give you some idea of what to expect.

How was the assignment made? Were you told merely to "read pages 246 to 283 in your text" or to "read material covering adjustment to frustration in normals, which you will find on pages 246 to 283 in your text?" Perhaps the way in which your instructor worded the assignment gives you the main idea for the reading task.

Does the instructor stay rather close to the text, expanding and clarifying it when necessary, or is the text assignment not to be covered in class except by quiz or examination of some type? In either case it is necessary for you to see the relationship between what you read and what is covered in class as a point of departure. In the first instance, a reconciliation between the instructor's presentation and the author's organization should not be too difficult. It becomes clear, then, that the acquisition of good reading notes in this situation requires not only that the text materials be condensed but that a way for reconciling these notes with class notes be established.

We shall assume that the best organization of content which you can adopt is the one used by the author, and we shall outline one possible system of note-taking which will satisfy the requirements stated above.

### Suggested Form for Reading Notes

In order to be maximally useful, reading notes

should be flexible, that is, they should permit addition, cross-referencing and rearrangement. You will find that you cannot close your notebook at the end of a science course and say, thankfully, "That's that!" You will refer to these notes over and over as you go into your clinical courses and may even find them useful later in your graduate work. For this reason, it is suggested that you use a loose-leaf binder rather than a stitched notebook from which pages cannot be removed. There are many attractive ring-binders available in 8½ inch by 11 inch filler size, with zippered outside fastenings and retractable handles which permit them to be carried like briefcases and to be opened out like notebooks. They have the advantages of being easily portable and of keeping the work on any one subject just as you left it. This size is also the one most useful for the inclusion of mimeographed materials, which are usually letter-sized. If you keep classes separated by tabular dividers which are appropriately labeled, you are sure of having what you need easily available in one notebook.

In order to follow the suggestions which will be given here, you will need *unlined* 8½ inch by 11 inch loose-leaf filler paper for all your courses. It should be noted that this is only *one* way of keeping reading notes which will satisfy our requirements. You may have an equally useful method already in operation. No one can devise a method which will work equally well for all users; so you should be alert for adaptations which will be better suited to your needs.

Place the paper so that the *holes are at the top*. Print the chapter number and title across the top of the page. It's a good idea to underline this in order to make it stand out. Next, rule two lines

5-1

CH. 5: BECOMING A MORE EFFICIENT NOTE-TAKER

| AUTHOR'S HEADINGS | MAIN IDEAS | COMMENTS |
|---|---|---|
| Reading to "learn the text" | | |
| Est. a frame of ref. | 1. Relationship to topics covered in class<br>2. Cues in wording of assignment | |
| Suggested form for reading notes | 1. Loose-leaf binder with tabular divisions | |

*across* the page about ¼ inch apart and lines *down* the page about 2 inches from each edge. Head the columns from left to right, "Author's Headings," "Main Ideas," and "Comments." Begin by recording the author's first section heading. Then, if a paragraph heading is given, record that next. Now read the paragraph, select the main ideas, and write these down in the second column. However, beware of being too brief lest you fail to understand your notes at a later rereading. Even if this does happen, it is a simple matter to refer back to the text under the particular paragraph or section heading. The inclusion of diagrams has been found helpful in subjects like anatomy. Continue in this way, paragraph by paragraph, until you have completed the chapter. To help you identify main ideas, you may wish to underline your text and/or make marginal notes as you go along.

Somewhere in this system a place must be assigned to record the full bibliographic information about the book which you are reading. This may appear on the first page of your reading notes, across the top of the page before you start with Chapter 1. It should include the author's name, the title, the name of the publisher, the place and date of publication, and the number of pages. Many students carry the author's name right along with every new chapter heading for identification purposes. The pages also should be numbered in sequence. One way of doing this which also identifies the chapter to which a particular page belongs is to record the number of the chapter index first, followed by the page within the chapter. For example, the second page of notes taken for chapter 5 would be numbered "5—2."

Of course the vocabulary cards mentioned in the preceding chapter go right along with this procedure. It is also a good idea to write on only one side of the page. This eliminates the problem of having to worry about which side of the page comes next when reviewing or rearranging your notes and provides room for insertions and additions without having to crowd these onto an already full page.

The third column headed "Comments" is for several uses: (1) your thoughts about what you are reading based on previous readings, class discussions, etc.; (2) your instructor's comments about the text materials which you may wish to summarize here (see section on "Note-Taking in Class"); (3) cross-references to other textbooks and/or source materials and (4) comments to help you in studying for exams (see chapter on "Becoming a More Efficient Test-Taker"). Some students have found it helpful to provide themselves with several pencils or ball-point pens of different colors, to permit a different color to be used for each type of comment.

## READING TO "COVER A TOPIC" BY USING SEVERAL ASSIGNED REFERENCES

In this situation, you not only have to locate pertinent materials and condense them but also have to combine ideas from several sources. Let us assume that you have been given four references to consult. The first step is to locate material pertinent to your topic in each reference by using the table of contents and the index. Then begin with the reference that appears to give the most complete coverage. One rough guide to this, although we recognize that this could be misleading, is the number of pages devoted to the topic in each reference after having made necessary adjustments for page size and details of format like width of margins, size of type, number of illustrations, etc.

### Making a Working Outline

Follow the procedure suggested previously for reading and summarizing main points for the most complete reference, with, however, these changes: (1) across the top of the page, print the topic; (2) make the heading 1½ inches wide and rule vertical lines at 2 inches and at 5 inches from the left side of the page; (3) across the top of the first two columns write the author's name, the title, the publisher's name, the place and date of publication, and the pertinent pages for the first reference as shown in the illustration:

TOPIC TO BE COVERED

Author, title, publisher, place, date, pages

| Headings | Main Ideas |
|---|---|
| | |

Some students have found it helpful, before continuing the analysis, to draw horizontal lines separating the main divisions or headings as indicated from the first source. This should provide a basis for a working outline into which the additional materials can be fitted.

### Analyzing Additional References

The remaining three references should be read now for similarities and differences and these systematically recorded in terms of the working outline, making additions as required. Next, select the reference with the (apparently) second fullest treatment of the topic. What are the possibilities which must be considered? These may be listed as follows: (1) this reference agrees with the first one in all important aspects, (2) this reference omits one or more items covered by the first one, (3) this reference includes one or more items not covered by the first one and (4) this reference holds a different point of view on one or more items from the first one.

Flip through the section and paragraph headings of the second reference to see which combination of these seems to be operating, and judge the width of the column to be alotted to this reference accordingly. At the top, in the 1½ inch heading, record the author's name, the title, etc., of this second reference. However, do not repeat the "headings" column again. Begin to read and as you do, think about the main ideas in the first paragraph. Do these agree with anything you have already recorded for the first reference? If so, simply check thus (√) on the appropriate line in the new column. If this is a brand new idea, record it in this new column, but space it below the last item appearing in the previous column for the first reference. The new paragraph or section heading may be placed in the left hand column with an arrow to show that it comes from the second source, thus:

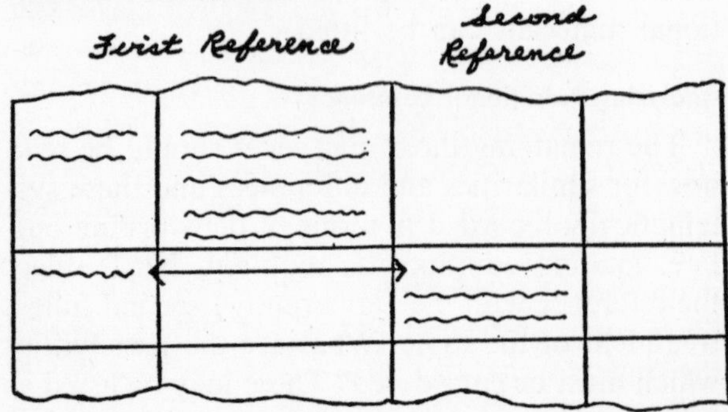


If the second reference covers a topic already recorded for the first but disagrees in point of view, this should be noted in the new column on the appropriate level, i.e., opposite the paragraph or section heading in the first column which covers it.

### Summarizing Results

An additionl page (or pages) may need to be added, both vertically to complete the content analysis and horizontally as new references are added. After the analysis is complete, a glance across horizontally to the particular headings indicates degree of agreement or disagreement among the references, while a glance down a column summarizes the presentation of a particular reference. In this connection, it is helpful to leave a column at the extreme right (perhaps 3 inches in width), in which summaries can be recorded.

## IMPROVING NOTE-TAKING IN CLASS

### How Does Your Instructor Proceed?

Although the note-taking system to be discussed here will work for any kind of classroom procedure, you can make it more useful by considering the following questions. Is there an outline for the course which the instructor follows in class? If so, this will provide you with at least a topical outline for your class notes. If not, then you will have to depend upon picking up your main headings from what the instructor says. Since many instructors begin the class by telling the students what they intend to cover, you should listen for this. It will also help to know whether or not you are expected to read "ahead of" or "behind" what goes on in class. If you are to read ahead, this content will give you clues about what is important.

### How Should Class Notes Be Set Up?

The most important reasons for taking class notes are: (1) to get the instructor's point of view, especially where this differs from the assigned textbooks and/or readings; (2) to get explanations for things which may not be clear in the text and (3) to record any content which is not in your text but which your instructor considers important in developing your understanding of the subject.

In order to accomplish these purposes, a flexible note-taking system should be set up again, preferably of the loose-leaf type which can be combined with the reading notes discussed in the preceding sections. This time, the headings might be "Instructor's Topic," "Main Ideas," and "Comments." For ease in handling and refiling, the sheets should be labeled with course number, date, and page number. Again, only one side of the paper should be used. In the "Comments" column, make notes to yourself for future follow-up, as for example, in reference to words to be looked up, or to questions which you hope your next reading session will clear up. If it does, simply put a line through the question, since the answer will appear in your reading notes, and cross-reference it to page number. If it is still unanswered after reading, make a note to ask the instructor at the next class meeting. In this column, too, may be recorded any hints given by the instructor about questions on tests, points of disagreement with texts, or suggested readings or cross-references.

You might like to take notes in class on a clipboard rather than in your notebook, especially since the suggested plan calls for holding the sheets so that the holes are at the top. It might be a good idea also to rule up a half-dozen sheets for each class meeting, to preclude the taking of class time to do this and thus running the risk of missing a main idea.

### How Much Should You Write Down?

The joke is often told about the student who

was so anxious to get down every pearl of wisdom that dropped from the instructor's lips that he even recorded "Good morning" at the beginning of every lecture! If the instructor is an orderly lecturer, it is fairly easy to follow the skeleton of

**Taking Down The Skeleton of the Lecture**

the lecture and to record the main ideas as they are expressed. Don't forget that a well-organized lecture is very much like the orderly development of a topic in a textbook; although ½ page may be devoted to it, it can be summarized in one or two well-chosen sentences. Try to listen to what the instructor says and then record only the main ideas. Even newspaper reporters, who are certainly responsible for detail, are not encouraged to learn shorthand, lest they miss the broad impact of what is being said.

If you have not been in the habit of taking notes in this way, it is possible that you may have a little trouble, especially at first, in listening to and then identifying the points to record. If this should happen, ask your instructor for an opportunity to check your class notes with him in conference and for suggestions on how to locate main points more successfully.

### How Should Notes On Class Questions Be Incorporated?

It may happen, especially if the instructor encourages it, that questions not related to the topic under discussion may be asked. These, if included in your class notes in the order in which students ask them, may be out of order as far as the development of the instructor's outline is concerned. Actually, you need to be able to file each question and its answer with the class notes dealing with that particular topic. There are several ways in which this might be done. One way is to use the back of the page on which the appropriate topic was developed. However, this is too time consuming to locate, and you might miss some of the discussion while leafing frantically through your notes for the proper page. Another way is to use separate sheets of paper for each question *on a different topic* and to file these in their appropriate places after class. This has the advantage of allowing you to devote your full attention to the question and answer, while still having the necessary flexibility.

### What About "Doodling"?

This is not really a good idea because it prevents your full concentration on the primary matter at hand, that of getting important ideas recorded in a systematic fashion for later reference. However, if you are an inveterate doodler and wish to continue this activity as a tension-reducing mechanism, it would be well for you to provide yourself with a special page just for doodling or with a smaller pad which can be devoted to this activity alone. Who knows?—you may find out a few things about yourself by examining your doodles in a particular class for a week!

### How Should Class Notes and Reading Notes Be Reconciled?

How you do this will depend largely on whether you find the topical outline in class to be more meaningful, and that the reading notes simply help to develop this, or the textbook outline to be better, and that the class notes are usually postscripts to it. In the latter case, it is probable that you are reading ahead of the instructor.

Depending on your feelings about this, you will use one or the other set of notes as the main set, and cross-reference it to the other. For example, if you feel that your reading notes are the more complete, then try to reconcile them with your class notes by indicating important points in the "Comments" column of your reading notes. Cross-reference notations can be made by using the abbreviation "cf." (from the Latin for "compare") as in "cf. class notes under .............. (topic) or .............. (page)."

It is a good idea first to reconcile and then to summarize your notes weekly, as concisely as possible, preferably by recording the really basic main ideas covered on a single sheet, with page references to your notes for each idea. This is excellent ongoing preparation for any quiz or test and forms the basis for organized studying for a test, as will be developed more fully in the next chapter.

# 6

# Becoming a More Efficient Test-Taker

Most of us dislike the idea of having to take tests, probably because we think of them only from the point of view of having our performance judged by the instructor who gives the test! Did you ever stop to think that tests also can be used by you for self-evaluation in very helpful ways? You want to be a nurse; your school wants you to be the best nurse possible in terms of what you and your instructors, *working together,* can achieve. Therefore, if you will try to adopt the point of view that tests provide you with an opportunity to see how well you, as a student nurse, agree with your instructors, who are the experts or specialists in nursing, on what is important to learn, you will get more out of the test situation than just a relatively painful experience. Let us now approach the problem of preparing for, taking, and making constructive use of, a test.

## WHAT KINDS OF TESTS ARE YOU LIKELY TO MEET?

### Test-makers

Probably you will have experience with both instructor-made tests and those made by professional test-making agencies. For example, your instructors probably will provide quizzes, "unit" tests (based on a meaningful unit of instruction), mid-terms and finals. The tests provided by professional agencies (usually referred to as "standardized" tests in contrast with "instructor-made" tests) include those which you may have taken prior to admission; those achievement tests in the various clinical areas and in related subjects, which are usually given at the end of a given course of instruction; and the State Board Licensing Examinations, prepared by the National League for Nursing.

### Kinds of Test Items or Questions

To begin with, these items may be classified as "performance" or "paper-and-pencil" types. The performance items require the demonstration of ability to *do* something, usually with apparatus or equipment of some kind. For example, in order to find out whether or not you have learned to use the microscope correctly, your instructor might ask you to focus on a particular slide and then check your setting himself. Paper-and-pencil items are usually divided into "essay-type" and "objective-type" categories. Among the various possibilities for essay questions are the "describe" type, as in "Describe the conditions that led to the Civil War in America."; and the "compare and contrast" type, as in "Compare and contrast communism and socialism." It is fairly obvious that two social science teachers, each reading the same student's response to the latter question, might grade it very differently. One teacher might be very sensitive to vocabulary level, grammar, punctuation, etc., while another may be inter-

EMERGENCY
J. McC.

ested chiefly in the ideas presented, regardless of whether or not they appear in complete, well-rounded sentences. Also, it is possible that these same two teachers even might apply different weights to the ideas presented, according to their different standards. For this reason, essay questions are sometimes called "subjective."

It was in an attempt to get away from the possibility of having a given response receive two different evaluations from equally competent raters that the so-called "objective" test items were formulated. There are many different types of objective test items, of which we shall illustrate the following: (1) completion, (2) multiple-choice with single right answer, (3) multiple-choice with multiple right answer, (4) true-false or yes-no and (5) matching.

### 1. Completion Item

The problem here is to insert one or more words, phrases, or clauses in indicated positions to form a complete sentence and true statement. For example, consider the item "Columbus discovered America in the year ..................." It would be ambiguous to word this "Columbus discovered America in ..................." because, as one enterprising student pointed out, you could equally well fill this in with "the Nina, the Pinta, and the Santa Maria"! Watch out for more than one possibility in completion items, and if you are in doubt, put them both down. You can explain to the instructor after the test is over why you did this.

If an instructor advises you to memorize textbook definitions for technical terms as the best way to increase your vocabulary accurately, then strategic words omitted from a definition might be a completion item to expect on a test or quiz.

### 2. Multiple-Choice Item With Single Right Answer*

In this type of item the test taker is presented with a question or an incomplete statement, with several choices being listed for answering the question or completing the statement, only one of which is correct. For example,

What is the relationship of 1/2 to 4/8?

1. Greater than
2. Equal to
3. Less than

The choice "none of the above," "some other value," or "some other answer" is used especially in problems involving computation to provide a way for the test taker to register his answer without getting any clues from the choices presented, no matter how unreasonable his computations turn out to be. It would be manifestly absurd to use this in the illustration above, since the three choices given exhaust the possibilities. However, consider the following example:

A rectangular draw-sheet is 54 inches wide and 108 inches long. What is its area in square yards?

1. 2 sq. yds.
2. 4½ sq. yds.
3. 5832 sq. yds.
4. None of the above.

The correct answer is 4½ square yards, most rapidly obtained by recognizing that 54 inches and 108 inches are equal to 1½ yards and 3 yards respectively, and then multiplying the

* You have already met items of this type in the chapter on "Becoming a More Efficient Reader."

length by the width. Of course, the correct answer would also be obtained, although not so rapidly, if one multiplied 54 x 108 and divided by 1296, the number of square inches in a square yard. However, suppose that in this last step a student mistakenly used 144 instead of 1296, and obtained 45 as the answer. If there were no such answer among the choices presented, this student would know that something was wrong and might spend valuable time trying to rectify his error, to the detriment of the correct answers to subsequent items he might have gotten with the same expenditure of time. However, with "none of the above" as a choice, he marks this one and goes on. In this way, it is argued, the inclusion of this choice works to the advantage of the test-taker.

### 3. Multiple-Choice Item With Multiple Right Answers

This type of item is very similar to the previous one. A question or an incomplete statement is presented, and several choices for answering the question or completing the statement are given. However, in this case more than one choice is correct; for example,

The fraction ½ has the same value as

1. 50 per cent
2. .05
3. 5/10
4. 500/1,000

In this problem choices 1, 3, and 4 are all correct. Another way of presenting this same problem which really puts it into the previous category of multiple-choice single right answer items is as follows:

Which of the following has the same value as the fraction ½?

A. 50 per cent
B. .05
C. 5/10
D. 500/1,000

1. All but A.
2. All but B.
3. All but C.
4. All but D.

In this form, choice 2 is correct. If choice B had been omitted from the item as presented above, the test-maker could have used "all of the above" as one choice (and the correct answer), and other choices of the type "A only," and "A and C," etc.

### 4. True-False or Yes-No Item*

This type of item is really a special case of the multiple-choice single right answer type, with the number of choices reduced to two. A statement is made which is to be judged either as true or false, or a question is asked which is to be answered either "yes" or "no." Usually, these items are more likely to be stated ambiguously than those with four or five choices. The test-taker frequently finds himself thinking, "Now, if by so-and-so they mean *this,* then it's true. However, if they mean *that,* then it's false. I wonder which they mean?" The most sensible thing to do in such a situation is to write a marginal note to the instructor, explaining your interpretation. You can tell him about this at the end of the examination period.

* You have already met items of this type in the chapter on "Budgeting Your Time."

Another thing to look for in these items is the use of words like "always" or "never." Most of the time, such statements are false, as for example, is question number 8 under "What is involved in reading?" in the chapter on "Becoming a More Efficient Reader."

### 5. Matching Item

In this type of item a column of words or descriptive phrases is presented, together with another column of choices. Each element of the first column is to be matched with an element in the second column, as for example,

| *Column 1* | *Column 2* |
|---|---|
| 1. Integer | A. 85/72 |
| 2. Decimal fraction | B. 146,957 |
| 3. Improper fraction | C. $\sqrt{15}$ |
| | D. ¼ |
| | E. .045 |

The number of choices in this illustration is greater than the number of items (1 to 3). In another form of this type, the same choice may be used more than once, or more than one choice may apply to a particular item, for example,

| *Column 1* | *Column 2* |
|---|---|
| 1. 85/72 | A. Integer |
| 2. 146,957 | B. Proper fraction |
| 3. ¼ | C. Improper fraction |
| 4. .045 | D. Decimal fraction |

In this case, choice B (proper fraction) applies to both ¼ and to .045 (since this is really 45/1,000 written decimally), while both choices B and D apply to .045.

## THE "CORRECTION FOR GUESSING"

Suppose that an individual is taking a test composed of multiple-choice with single right answer type of items. It is then possible for this individual to pick the right answer to a certain number of items purely by guessing, without really knowing anything about the subject matter being tested. A consideration of the probabilities of doing this under certain assumptions has resulted in the so-called "correction for guessing," which is given as follows:

> To obtain the score, subtract from the number of correct answers a fraction of the incorrect answers, this fraction having for its denominator one less than the number of choices.

Thus, if R stands for the number of right answers, W for the number of wrong answers and K for the number of choices, then the score S is given by the formula:

$$S = R - \frac{W}{K - 1}$$

In the case of 5-choice items, this means that the score is equal to "rights minus ¼ wrongs," while for true-false items, the formula reduces to "rights minus wrongs."

It is obvious that if a correction for guessing is to be applied, this will guide you in deciding what to do if you really don't know the answer. For a 5-choice item, you gain a point if you guess right and lose ¼ point if you guess wrong. On standardized tests you will find a statement about guessing in the directions for taking the test, either to the effect that you should ". . . work as rapidly and as accurately as you can, for your score will be the number of correct answers . . ." (in which case no correction for guessing will be applied so there is no penalty for an incorrect hunch), or ". . . you may answer items even if you are not perfectly sure of the correct response, but you should avoid *wild guessing,* since your score will be the number of your correct responses diminished by a fraction of your incorrect responses . . ." (in which case there *is* a correction for guessing).

For a teacher-made test, if you have been told in class that it will be of the multiple-choice type, it is a good idea to find out from the instructor whether there is only one right answer to each item or more than one; and whether or not a correction for guessing will be made. If you have failed to do this ahead of time, and the directions for taking the test do not include the scoring formula, you should check with the instructor during the test period, although this is far less desirable than to have done so prior to the test.

## STUDYING FOR A TEST

There are some considerations which are basic to studying for a test, regardless of what type of test it is to be. While it is true that essay-type tests aim to measure your ability to select and organize pertinent information, and that objective-type tests are designed largely to measure your "recognition" of the right answer, that word "recognition" can cover quite a variety of mental gymnastics, as you already may have had occasion to observe. It has been remarked that one cannot consistently choose the correct one among five choices without knowing a little something about the areas being tested! The following suggestions are therefore presented as possible helps in preparing to take a test. Again, remember that these are to be modified to meet your particular needs.

The basic assumptions in these suggestions are that your instructor, in the role of content-expert or specialist, is presenting materials which it is necessary that you make part of your professional equipment if you wish to be a "good" nurse and that the extent to which you and your instructor agree on what is important (via the test situation) may be taken by you as one indication of how well you are progressing toward your mutual goal.

### Reconcile Class Notes and Reading Notes

Your instructor gives you at least two indications of what is considered important: (1) class lectures and discussions and (2) assigned readings and other tasks. The first logical step in preparing for a test, then, is to get these two sources of information together in the most usable form. It has been suggested already in the previous chapter on "Becoming a More Efficient Note-taker" that this be done weekly, using either the class notes or the reading notes as a point of departure, depending on which set of notes is the more complete and the better organized. Also, it has been suggested that a weekly summary sheet of main points be made, based on your reconciliation of the two sources. If you have not been doing this as you go along, then such a reconciliation and summary are your first tasks.

### If You Were the Instructor, What Would You Ask?

Your instructor may have given you some hints in class like, "This is very important"; or "No good nurse would fail to know that—"; or even "This would be a good thing to ask on a test!" These points should have been noted in the "Comments" column of your class notes to permit their being picked up easily now. A more subtle way of getting clues to what the instructor thinks especially important is to look at the length of time spent in class on a given topic. However, there should be a warning issued here; it is sometimes necessary to spend a disproportionate amount of time in class laying a foundation for later topics which are more important, but which will go more quickly for having had a good basis established.

At this point it would be well to work with your weekly summaries, which have reconciled class and reading notes, and to distil these further for the home stretch. The use of a colored pencil to underline important points would be helpful here in noting what you want to pick up for your final distillate. In making this, try to put yourself in the position of an instructor. How would you outline these materials if you were going to teach them to other students like yourself? What would you ask them on a test? It's something like the old story of the farmer and his runaway horse. The farmer tried to think where the horse would go if he got the chance; the farmer went there, and sure enough—there was the horse!

You might begin with the main topics covered, and the main ideas under each topic. Now from where you sit, what is *really* the most important of all these important points? It very often happens that while in the midst of a reading assignment, you focus on more details than you will need now, since some learning on your part has taken place. You might now make a new outline of these highly selected points, using headings like "Topic," "Main Ideas" and "Cues." This last column is for any key words or phrases or memory helps you want to rig for yourself.

It is not usually a good idea to use what are called "mnemonic" devices, such as a nonsense word made by stringing together the first letters of key words or phrases. There are two risks involved here; (1) since the word is really meaningless, you are having to learn one more thing besides the materials you are really interested in retaining, and you may forget the magic word and (2) if the word, though bizarre, is really pronounceable, you may find yourself remembering the word but not what it is supposed to represent. For example, back in the 1920's elementary school students were encouraged to learn the nonsense term "St. Wapniacl" made from the first letters of the Presidential cabinet offices in the order of their creation, thus: State, Treasury, War, etc. To their dismay, many of the teachers learned, when they gave a test, that the names of the cabinet offices in the order of creation were "St. Wapniacl" for quite a few students, who could remember the crutch but not what it stood for! The moral of this story is that if you organize your material meaningfully, you should be able to contrive meaningful memory helps in terms of key words, phrases, and ideas.

### "Cramming" Versus Spaced Study

In connection with learning a technical vocabulary, the point already has been made that you will tend to remember better if you go over your vocabulary cards as many times as possible and with time intervals between. The same thing is true of studying for a test. If the suggestions made about the weekly reconciling of class and

**The Unfortunate After-Effects of Cramming**

reading notes with weekly summaries are followed, you are really doing ongoing preparation for any test which might be announced.

In your high school courses, you may not have seen the long-range value of some of the content you were being asked to learn, so that perhaps the routine of cramming just for the exam (and then forgetting the whole thing immediately after handing in your paper) served you to your satisfaction. However, your situation now is very different. Everything you are being asked to learn has a bearing on your professional goal; in order to attain this goal, you must not only graduate creditably but also pass the State Board Licensing Examinations. You can no longer afford test-preparation technics that permit you to forget easily.

The more frequently you go over your summary *in meaningful terms,* the more likely it is to become part of your available body of knowledge in that content area. As you read over your summary, you will also tend to remember better if you read aloud, since then you will be getting a double stimulus: visual and auditory.

In reproducing their outlines, many students find it helpful to test themselves by taking a blank piece of paper, and after giving themselves the main topics, then seeing how well they can fill in the main ideas under each topic. If you find that you have missed an idea, concentrate on that idea *in its relation to the other ideas* under that topic rather than on the idea alone, so that you will learn it in a meaningful setting.

## TAKING A TEST

### Suggested Pre-test Behavior

1. Get a good night's sleep before the day of the test.

2. If possible, review your summary as soon as you get up in the morning and again just before going into the test situation.

3. Present yourself for the test sufficiently ahead of time to get settled but not so early that your carefully achieved mental organization of content can be upset by frenzied last-minute questions and comments from your classmates.

4. Settle yourself as comfortably as possible, and arrange your personal effects. Place your watch where you can see it easily.

5. If your instructor permits (and you should check ahead of time), bring your favorite hard candy to help relieve your tension and/or hunger during the test.

### Suggested Test Behavior

1. If you have trouble getting started on tests, or if you have a few main ideas you'd like to jot down before they leave your mind, turn your test paper over as soon as you get it and write these things down on the back. This provides the necessary "self-starter" and you can then go on to the test proper.

2. For essay-type tests:

A. Read the entire set of questions over first, noting the score value of each. Apportion your available time on the basis of these values.

B. Tackle first those questions that count the most. Make an outline of points you want to include in each question, with main and subheadings. Since the questions tell you the topics you will have to cover, you can decide where you will use your information and illustrations to best advantage. If there seems to be an overlap between questions, try not to use exactly the same illustration for both.

C. Depending on how your instructor will grade, it may be profitable to do all of your outlining first for all questions before beginning to develop any. You should check with your instructor to find out whether partial credit will be given for an outline. If so, it would be better to use a sentence outline rather than the more cryptic word-and-phrase outline, which might be perfectly clear to you but might not be so meaningful to your instructor.

D. Keep a sharp look-out on time. It usually pays off better score-wise to develop all questions as far as you possibly can from your outlines under your self-imposed time limits than to use all of your time in lovingly polishing one to perfection! You may find that you were overgenerous in your allotments on one or two questions, in which event you can use the additional time to go back to ones you wish to develop further.

E. If your instructor permits, use a separate sheet or page for each question. Just as in keeping your class and reading notes flexible, it is a good idea to make it possible to go back and forth, adding where you wish.

3. For objective-type tests:

A. Decide what to do about guessing. (The directions for taking the test should help you.)

B. Speed counts. Read through the questions as quickly as possible, answering those you feel you know, and putting a dash (—) or some other mark in front of the item-number of those you are omitting on this first round.

C. Go back over the items marked by the dash and try to answer them. As you answer a particular item, put a line through the dash to indicate that you have coped with this item (+).

D. If you have time and need to go back for

a third round, for those items still not answered, do so.

E. The question of whether or not to change your first answer on a second reading has been studied. The results indicate that most people lose more points than they gain by making these changes. If you want to study this for yourself, keep a record of the answers you change on several tests, and see whether this is also true for you.

### A Note On "Beating The Test-scoring Machine"

You will be taking standardized tests, recording your answers on separate answer sheets which will be scored by an electrical test-scoring machine. Remember that any schemes which enterprising students can think up for "beating the machine" have already been provided for by the agency which will score the tests! For example, if the test is of the 5-choice single right answer type, some students have thought that the way to proceed when you don't know the right answer is to mark all 5 choices—one of them is bound to be right! While this is true, let us see how this is controlled in scoring. The machine is set to deduct ¼ point for each wrong answer and to add 1 point for each right answer. Therefore, it will add one point for the right choice (whatever it may be), but it will also deduct 4 times ¼ or one point for the 4 incorrect marks, thus netting exactly zero for that item!

A far better idea is to narrow down your choices to 2. This is often possible, especially in verbal items where you feel that either one of 2 choices is IT but can't tell which one. In this case, it is reasoned, you will get one point for the correct one and lose ¼ point for the incorrect one, thereby netting ¾ of a point for your efforts, which is better than having left the item blank. However, here again the scoring agency is prepared. Before papers are given to the scoring clerks to be inserted in the machine, they are inspected manually for multiple markings. Any items having 2 or more marks are red-penciled, and the paper is then *hand-scored,* omitting these items. It would be well to remember that the motto of these agencies is "There is nothing new under the sun"!

### Suggested Post-test Behavior

Recalling that the suggested point of view is that tests provide a means for you to validate your opinion about what is important with the opinions of specialists, we offer the following suggestions:

1. Note in your summary outline any important points appearing on the test which you omitted.
2. If there is to be a class postmortem of the test, item for item, note down the correct answers to the items you missed, and incorporate these into your summary for future reference. If there is to be no class discussion, look up the answers yourself and incorporate them into your summary.
3. If you were far afield on what you thought your instructor was going to ask, seek a conference with him as soon as possible. Bring your class and reading notes, your summaries, etc., and explain how you went about preparing for the test. Ask for suggestions for improving your technic.

**Are you in control when working with numbers?**

# 7

# Improving Arithmetic Skills

If you are of the opinion that arithmetic skills, although necessary for nursing students because of their science courses, are of little importance to the graduate nurse, you should correct this immediately! It is certainly true that as a student you will have to cope with problems involving balancing equations, calculating pressure and volume, etc. It is equally true that as a graduate you will have to calculate drug dosages rapidly and accurately. A patient in difficulty cannot wait for half-an-hour while you count on your fingers to find out what to do with the available dosage in terms of the dosage in the doctor's orders! It is not difficult to learn a few basic operations, and even those who "simply *can't* do math" have been known to master them without too much difficulty.

However, it may well be that you already possess the necessary skills, in which case you may wish to go on to the next chapter. In order to help you find out whether or not this is so, the following set of questions is presented.

## HOW ARE YOUR ARITHMETIC SKILLS?

Work each of the following problems, and indicate your answer by putting an X over the correct response. You may use scratch paper for your calculations.

1. Reduce 30/45 to lowest terms.
   A. 2/3 B. 6/9 C. 5/9 D. Some other value
2. Multiply 6 by 2/3
   A. 3 B. 18 C. 24 D. Some other value
3. Multiply 2/3 by 5/6
   A. 2/9 B. 4/5 C. 5/9 D. Some other value
4. Divide 1/4 by 2
   A. 1/2 B. 1/8 C. 8 D. Some other value
5. Divide 1/3 by 1/4
   A. 1/12 B. 3/4 C. 1 1/3 D. Some other value
6. The doctor orders 1/6 gr. of morphine sulfate and the tablets on hand are 1/4 gr. How many tablets are required?
   A. 2/3 B. 1 1/4 C. 1/24 D. Some other value
7. Find x in the following:
   $$3 : x = 1 : 5$$
   A. 1-2/3 B. 3/5 C. 15 D. Some other value
8. Find x in the following:
   $$8 : 3 = x : 4$$
   A. 9 B. 6 C. 2/3 D. Some other value
9. How many minims of a 5 gr. caffeine and sodium benzoate solution should be given from an ampule containing 7½ gr. in 30 minims of solution?
   A. 20 B. 1.25 C. 45 D. Some other value
10. The doctor orders 5 units of ACTH. The vial contains 25 units of ACTH dissolved in 60

minims. How many minims should you give?
A. 1/5 B. 5 C. 12 D. Some other value

You will find the correct answers given at the end of the chapter under *Arithmetic Skills Pretest*. If your score is not perfect, you will find help in the following sections as indicated below.

| Number of Problem Incorrectly Solved | Refer to Section Headed |
|---|---|
| 1 | WORKING WITH FRACTIONS: **Reducing to Lowest Terms** |
| 2, 3 | WORKING WITH FRACTIONS: **Multiplication** |
| 4, 5 | WORKING WITH FRACTIONS: **Division** |
| 6 | DOSAGE PROBLEMS INVOLVING WHOLE NUMBERS AND FRACTIONS |
| 7 to 10 | DOSAGE PROBLEMS INVOLVING RATIO AND PROPORTION |

## SOME BASIC FACTS, TERMS, AND OPERATIONS

Since the solution of problems like the ones given in the pretest requires a knowledge of how to work with whole numbers and fractions, a systematic though brief review of these will be given here, followed by another test. If you need further work after the completion of the post-test, an indication of your area of difficulty will be given again.

### Mixed Numbers and Fractions: Some Definitions

#### *Common Fraction*

A common fraction is one which has one or more equal parts of a unit expressed by two numbers: (1) the *numerator,* which is the number of equal parts taken and (2) the *denominator,* which is the number of equal parts into which the unit is divided. The numerator and the denominator are called the *terms* of the fraction.

Example: $\frac{3}{4}$ 3 (numerator) / 4 (denominator)

When working with fractions, it is important to remember that 1/2 is larger than 1/3 or 1/6, that is, the larger the number of parts into which a unit is divided (denominator), the smaller is any one part. This sometimes provides a common-sense check to the answer which you obtain to a problem. If you have only ¼ grain tablets to begin with, and the dosage specified is ½ grain,

it will do no good to give any part of the 1/4 grain tablet, since 1/2 is larger than 1/4.

### *Proper Fraction*

A proper fraction is one whose numerator is less than its denominator.

Example: 1/2, 5/8

### *Improper Fraction*

An improper fraction is one whose numerator is equal to or greater than its denominator.

Example: 4/4, 8/5, 9/8

### *Mixed Number*

The term mixed number denotes a whole number and a fraction used together.

Example: 2 1/4, 3 1/2, 4 3/4

## WORKING WITH FRACTIONS

### Reducing to Lowest Terms

To reduce a common fraction (either proper or improper) to its lowest terms, divide both numerator and denominator by the largest number that will evenly divide both terms. For example, to reduce 30/45 to lowest terms (Problem 1 of pretest), it is not enough to recognize that 5 will "go into" both 30 and 45 evenly, thus getting 6/9, because 6/9 can now be reduced if you divide both numerator and denominator by 3. While 5 and 3 are certainly divisors, neither one alone is the *largest* common divisor. Now try the problems in Exercise 1. You will find the correct answers given at the end of the chapter.

Exercise 1: Reduce to lowest terms:

A. 24/56

B. 27/63
C. 54/30
D. 120/125

### Multiplication

The general rule for multiplying two fractions together is to multiply the numerators first, then the denominators, and then to reduce the resulting fraction to lowest terms. It is sometimes possible to make your work easier by "cancelling out" before you multiply, as follows:

$$\frac{\not{2}}{3} \times \frac{5}{\underset{3}{\not{6}}} = \frac{5}{9}$$

(Problem 3 in pretest)

You could have obtained this also by following the rule exactly, as follows:

$$2/3 \times 5/6 = 10/18 = 5/9$$

Now try the problems in Exercise 2. You will find the correct answers given at the end of the chapter.

Exercise 2: Multiply the following fractions:

A. 3/4 × 2/6
B. 2/5 × 3/4
C. 5/8 × 5/6
D. 4/5 × 3/4

If you consider that whole numbers can be written as improper fractions with 1 in the denominator, the rule given for the multiplication of two fractions will work equally well for the multiplication of a fraction by a whole number. In this case the rule reduces to multiplying the numerator by the whole number, retaining the denominator intact, and reducing the resulting fraction to lowest terms, as follows:

$$6 \times 2/3 = 6/1 \times 2/3 = 12/3 = 4$$

(Problem 2 in pretest)

Now try the problems in Exercise 3. You will find the correct answers given at the end of the chapter.

Exercise 3: Multiply the following:

A. $5 \times 4/2$
B. $4 \times 2/3$
C. $3 \times 7/8$
D. $3 \times 3/4$

#### Division

The general rule for dividing one fraction by another is to invert the terms of the divisor, and then proceed as in multiplication, remembering to reduce the resulting fraction to lowest terms. For example, in the problem $1/3 + 1/4$, the divisor is $1/4$. If this is inverted, it becomes $4/1$. The problem then is $1/3 \times 4/1$ which is $4/3$ or $1 = 1/3$. (Pretest problem number 5.)

Now try the problems in Exercise 4. You will find the correct answers given at the end of the chapter.

Exercise 4: Divide as indicated in each of the following:

A. $3/5 \div 1/3$
B. $3/4 \div 7/8$
C. $2/3 \div 5/7$
D. $5/9 \div 4/5$

If you recall that whole numbers can be written as improper fractions with 1 in the denominator, the rule given for division of fractions will work equally well for the division of a fraction by a whole number, for example, $1/4 \div 2$ may be considered as $1/4 \div 2/1$ which becomes $1/4 \times 1/2$ or $1/8$. (Pretest problem number 4.)

Now try the problems in Exercise 5. You will find the correct answers given at the end of the chapter.

Exercise 5: Perform the indicated divisions:

A. $5/7 \div 4$
B. $4/5 \div 2$
C. $2/3 \div 3$
D. $5/6 \div 4$

## DOSAGE PROBLEMS INVOLVING WHOLE NUMBERS AND FRACTIONS

How does a nurse need to use these arithmetical skills as she works with medications? Most tablets, capsules, and pills come in definite doses designed for immediate use. However, there are still many situations in which the nurse needs to know either how many tablets or what portion of a tablet she must prepare in order to administer the required dosage of a drug.

Suppose, for example, that the doctor orders 1/6 gr. of morphine sulfate and that the tablets on hand are in 1/4 gr. doses. Since 1/6 is less than 1/4, the nurse must administer a portion of a tablet. The question is, what portion? (Pretest problem number 6.)

The rule which applies for problems of this type is to *divide the dose desired by the dose on hand* to determine the part of a tablet or the number of tablets required.

Thus, working through the problem, we have $1/6 \div 1/4$ or $1/6 \times 4/1$ or $2/3$ of a tablet.

Now try the problems in Exercise 6. You will

find the correct answers given at the end of the chapter.

Exercise 6: Find the number of tablets or the portion of a tablet in each of the following situations:

A. The doctor orders 1/160 gr. of Ergotrate and the tablets on hand are 1/320 gr.

B. The doctor orders 1/200 gr. of atropine sulfate and the tablets on hand are 1/150 gr.

## DOSAGE PROBLEMS INVOLVING RATIO AND PROPORTION

It is sometimes necessary for a nurse to obtain the correct dosage of a drug from a stock solution of a given strength, or to give to a patient only a portion of an ampule or vial of medication. The problem here is to determine how much of the stock solution will contain the required dosage of a given medication. For example, suppose that the stock solution of caffeine sodium benzoate contains 7½ gr. in 30 minims of solution and that the required dosage is 5 gr. How many minims of stock solution should be given? (Pretest problem number 9.)

Let us now recall two additional terms which will be useful to us here. *Ratio* is a way of expressing the relationship of one quantity to another and may be written with a colon between the two quantities or as a fraction. For example, 7½ gr. in 30 minims could be written as 7½ : 30 or as 7½/30, and 5 gr. in x minims (we use "x" here to indicate that we do not know this value, but wish to find it) could be written as 5 : x or as 5/x.

If we set two ratios equal to each other, this expression is called a *proportion*. For example, consider the fractions 1/2 and 3/6, which are equal. This may be written as $1 : 2 = 3 : 6$. The first and last terms are called the *extremes* (1 and 6), and the second and third terms are called the *means* (2 and 3). In a proportion, it is always true that *the product of the means equals the product of the extremes* ($2 \times 3 = 1 \times 6$).

Returning now to our problem, we want 5 gr. to have the same relationship to x minims that 7½ gr. has to 30 minims, that is to say,

$$5 : x = 7.5 : 30$$
$$7.5x = 150$$
$$x = 20$$

We can state this as a rule in the following terms:

Dose desired : x amount of solution desired =
drug on hand : solution on hand.

This is an easier way of following through on the tablet rule which would give us:

$$\frac{5}{x} \div \frac{7.5}{30} \text{ or } \frac{5}{x} \times \frac{30}{7.5} = \frac{150}{7.5}, \text{ whence } x = 20.$$

Now try the problems in Exercise 7. You will find the correct answers given at the end of the chapter.

Exercise 7: Find the correct dosage in each of the following situations:

A. The doctor ordered 5 units of ACTH. The vial contains 25 units of ACTH dissolved in 60 minims. How many minims should you give? (Pretest problem 10.)
B. The doctor ordered 75 mg. of Demerol. The ampule contains 100 mg. of Demerol in 2 cc. How many cc. should you give?

Remember to look coldly at your answer in terms of what has been requested. An answer to the last problem of 2 = 2/3 is obviously wrong; common sense will reveal that there is *more* Demerol in 2 = 2/3 cc. than in 2 cc. You are looking for *less* Demerol; namely, 75 mg.

Now you are ready for the final round. How well have you reinstated your skills in the area of fractions, whole numbers and ratio and proportion? Try the following post-test and find out.

## NOW HOW ARE YOUR ARITHMETIC SKILLS?

Work each of the following problems and indicate your answer by putting an X over the correct response. You may use scratch paper for your calculations.

1. Reduce 48/72 to lowest terms.
   A. 4/6 B. 6/9 C. 12/18 D. Some other value
2. Multiply 4 by 2/6.
   A. 1 1/3 B. 8 C. 12 D. Some other value
3. Multiply 5/9 by 3/7.
   A. 15/63 B. 5/21 C. 35/27 D. Some other value
4. Divide 5/8 by 6.
   A. 3 = 3/4 B. 9 = 3/5 C. 5/48 D. Some other value
5. Divide 2/9 ÷ 7/8.
   A. 7/36 B. 16/63 C. 3 15/16 D. Some other value
6. The doctor orders 1/20 gr. of Dilandid and the tablets on hand are 1/16 gr. How many tablets are required?
   A. 4/5 B. 1 = 1/4 C. 1/320 D. Some other value
7. Find x in the following:
   5 : x = 4 : 16
   A. 1/20 B. 12 = 4/5 C. 20 D. Some other value

8. Find x in the following:

   $$1.5 : x = 5 : 24$$

   A. 7 = 1/5 B. 72 C. 80 D. Some other value
9. The doctor orders 32 units of regular insulin. The bottle contains 40 units of regular insulin in 15 minims. How many minims should you give?

   A. 4/5 B. 18 = 3/4 C. 120 D. Some other value
10. The doctor orders 75 mg. of Demerol. The ampule contains 250 mg. of Demerol in 5 cc. How many cc. should you give?

    A. 2/3 B. 15 C. 16 = 2/3 D. Some other value

If your score is still not perfect, you may wish to work additional problems of similar types in other sources. Probably you will find help in your school library by locating elementary algebra textbooks for additional explanation of the theory of ratio and proportion and pharmacology textbooks for additional verbal problems dealing with dosage.

## ANSWERS TO PROBLEMS

### Answers to Arithmetic Skills Pretest

1. A.
2. D.
3. C.
4. B.
5. C.
6. A.
7. C.
8. D.
9. A.
10. C.

### Answers to Exercise 1: Reducing to Lowest Terms

A. 3/7
B. 3/7
C. 1-4/5
D. 24/25

Answers to Exercise 2: Multiplication of Fractions

A. 1/4
B. 3/10
C. 25/48
D. 3/5

Answers to Exercise 3:
Multiplication of Fraction By Whole Number

A. 10
B. 2-2/3
C. 2-5/8
D. 2-1/4

Answers to Exercise 4: Division of Fractions

A. 1-4/5
B. 6/7
C. 14/15
D. 25/36

Answers to Exercise 5:
Division of Fraction By Whole Number

A. 5/28
B. 2/5
C. 2/9
D. 5/24

Answers to Exercise 6:
Problems Involving Whole Numbers and Fractions

A. 2 tablets
B. 3/4 tablet

Answers to Exercise 7:
Problems Involving Ratio and Proportion

A. 12 minims
B. 1-1/2 cc.

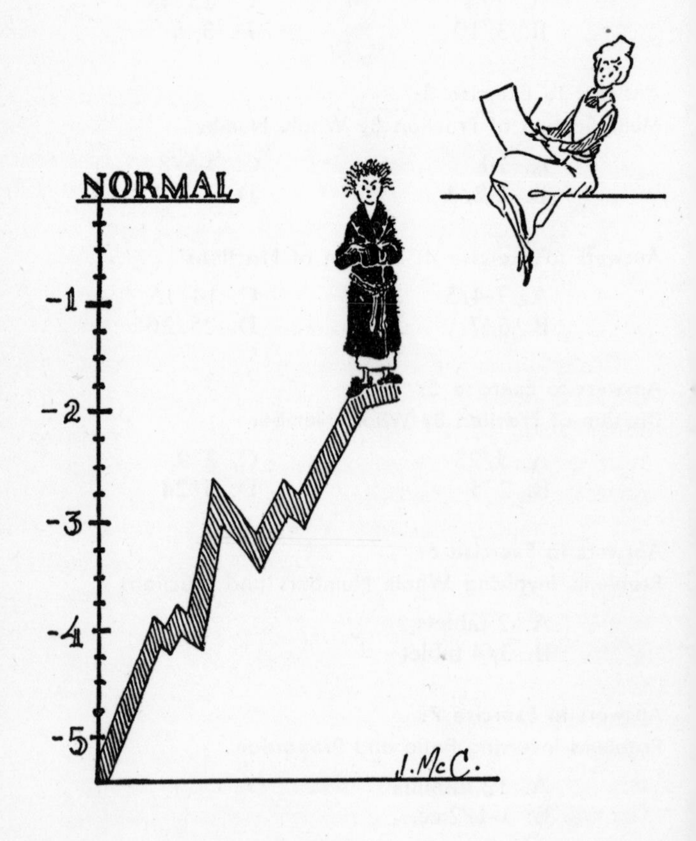
NORMAL
-1
-2
-3
-4
-5
J.McC.

# 8

# Improving Your Observational Skills

Observation is the basis for most of our objective data about behavior of individuals from birth to death and of so-called "normals" and "deviates from normality." If we consider well persons as normal, then illness, both mental and physical, can be considered as a deviation from the normal, and we may infer that good observational skills must be part of the equipment of every professional nurse. The appearance and the behavior of the patient, his reactions to nursing care, his feelings about himself and his environment—these are some of the kinds of things the nurse looks for in her attempt to evaluate the effectiveness of the nursing care being given the patient. On the basis of such observations, it is possible that radical changes may be made in the nursing care plan in the best interests of the patient's progress.

## WHAT IS THE OBSERVATIONAL TASK?

### Characteristics of a "Good" Observation

The observed behavior should bear a direct relationship to the purpose for making the observation (validity). For example, if you wanted to see how 5-year-old Johnny interacted with others of his age group, you would observe him with other 5-year-olds, rather than with adults, adolescents, older children, or infants. If the doctor's orders called for observing the patient for signs of dyspnea, your technical knowledge of this condition would tell you what to look for.

Also, there should be some assurance that the observation has been reported accurately (reliability); for example, that the thermometer has been read correctly and the pulse counted correctly, etc. One way of checking on this is to see whether another competent observer would report the same results in a similar situation.

### Components of the Task

The observational task may be considered in terms of the following sequence:

1. Define what is to be observed in terms of the purpose for the observation. (WHAT.)
2. Plan the observation. (HOW, WHEN, WHERE.)
3. Make the observation.
4. Record the observation in objective terms.
5. Check the validity and reliability of the observational data.
6. Take action.

#### DEFINING WHAT IS TO BE OBSERVED

Let us consider the case of Jill, who was reported by both her first- and second-grade teachers as being "a trouble-maker, unable to get along with other children, and very aggressive." Both teachers included anecdotal records of some of

Jill's "aggressive" behavior. One teacher gave as an illustration Jill's "apparently unprovoked attack with her fists" on a boy after they had been in conversation for about a minute in a playground situation, although no indication was given of the subject of the conversation nor of what the boy might have said to provoke her! The other teacher gave as her illustration the fact that when Shirley "tagged" Jill during the playground period, Jill "turned on her fiercely with screams and chased the poor child several times around the school yard." Again, there is a difference in the type of "tagging" done, as we can certainly recall from our own tagging days—all the way from the "love-tap" to really letting the other child have it! These illustrations point up the need for defining what is to be observed in *operational terms*—not merely observing for "signs of aggression, but precisely formulating exactly what type of behavior, in what kind of situation, is to be considered as a sign of aggression. We can then reformulate the first step as

DEFINE WHAT IS TO BE OBSERVED OPERATIONALLY IN TERMS OF THE PURPOSE FOR THE OBSERVATION

In a nursing situation, you will have assistance in doing this not only from your own technical knowledge of what is involved in a particular disease and/or condition but also from the doctor's diagnosis and orders, and from the previous nurses' notes. These must all be considered in making your nursing care plan for (and with) your patient.

## PLANNING THE OBSERVATION

### How

Who is to make the observation? Will there be a single observer, or will more than one be required in order to provide a reliability check? (In your beginning ward experiences, you will probably be using your instructor to check on the accuracy of your procedures.) The argument for the multiple-observer technic goes something like this. While observer No. 1 is writing down his observation, it is possible that he is missing something vital; therefore we should introduce observer No. 2 since it is not likely that they would both be writing at precisely the same instant. It is clear that anything reported by both observer No. 1 and observer No. 2 can be accepted with considerable confidence as having really occurred. However, what is to be done with items reported by one but not by the other? Therefore, we should introduce observer No. 3 into the situation and accept items reported by at least two out of the three observers.

It is quite possible, however, that a phalanx of three observers entering a situation might so alter the behavior of the subjects that the validity of the data becomes questionable. A group of children might accept one person without serious disruption, but three people is another story. Of course, if the situation permits the observers to remain hidden, as in a one-way vision screen setup, this objection is removed.

How are the observational data to be recorded? Will this be done manually, or are there mechanical aids available such as movies or tape-recorders? If either of these is to be used, the patient's permission should be obtained (or the permission of the legal guardian if the patient is a minor or a mental incompetent). There is danger here, too, of affecting the validity of the data; we may not get typical behavior from the subject if he knows he is being photographed or recorded. Some researchers have tried to overcome this difficulty by "getting the subjects used to" being photographed and/or recorded *before* actually beginning the collection of data. However, this is a relatively costly and time-consuming process and should be considered carefully in terms of the benefits to be derived. Then, too, there is always the possibility of mechanical breakdown at a crucial point; a new tape or film may be needed or the camera or recorder may cease to function.

It must be recalled that the ultimate purpose for most of these observations is the formulation of some kind of action plan. Teachers should get more insight into how to handle behavior problems; nurses should have a better basis for evaluating and possibly changing their nursing care plans, etc. Therefore, the data need to be transcribed or transferred in some usable form from the film or tape to a basis for making action plans. This, too, is usually a costly and time-consuming process. It is because of considerations like these that so much hand-recording of observational data is being done at the present time.

### When

What time of day or night is best for making the observation? This may be predetermined already by hospital routines; or may be specifically indicated in the doctor's orders; or may be an outgrowth of the previous nurses' notes; or may depend solely on your nursing knowledge.

### Where

In what kind of setting is the observation to be made? For example, do you want the patient in or out of bed, and in what position?

## MAKING THE OBSERVATION

### Introducing Yourself Into the Situation

In order for the patient to make maximum progress it is necessary that a good basis for a therapeutic relationship be established between patient and nurse-personnel. Of major importance in this connection are the kinds of feelings the patient has about nurses and nursing, the hospital, being sick, etc. Obviously, anyone who gives any kind of nursing care to the patient in the present situation, as well as anyone who has done so in the past, makes a contribution to the patient's overall feelings. As you can see, your part in this picture is quite an important one. You can contribute to the positive feeling of "nurses are comforting people to have around; you can trust them; they are pleasant and understanding and treat you like a human being"; or to the negative feeling "nurses do things to hurt you without telling you why; they treat you like a dog; they are not to be trusted."

If you are meeting the patient for the first time, a good beginning is to introduce yourself and explain the purpose for your visit. Since you already know the patient's name (from the assignment) you are in the driver's seat socially. "Good morning, Mrs. X. I am Miss Y. and I have come to ..................."

### Getting the Patient's Co-operation

Depending on the situation, explain to the patient what you are going to do and why and what co-operation you expect from him. This may range all the way from none at all, if the patient is comatose, to visiting the bathroom alone while you remake the bed. A specimen may be required as the basis for further observation, or you may be going to carry out a procedure as part of the nursing care plan. If the patient can expect any pain or discomfort either during or after the procedure, this should be explained and the patient prepared for it. This not only helps to establish a feeling of trust, but as far as our observational situation is concerned, it also lays the groundwork for more accurate data less contaminated by "red-herrings" not pertinent to the situation.

If you plan to make notes during your conversation with the patient, this, too, should be explained in such terms as "I don't want to run the risk of forgetting this," or "I'm doing this so the next person to give you nursing care will know what we did and how you feel about it."

### Removing Yourself From the Situation

Once you have completed your collection of observational data, you need to remove yourself in such a way that the patient will have as positive feelings as possible toward the next observation (or observer). Some indication of when this is likely to be and of who is likely to make the observation, as well as an expression of concern for present and future comfort, usually is given to end the observation on a positive note. "Would you like to read your book now? Miss Z., who relieves me, will be looking in on you around —— o'clock. Do you have everything you need? . . . Good-by until tomorrow."

Of course, the interpersonal relationships involved have been oversimplified because the primary purpose of this chapter is to discuss observational skills. As you work with your instructors in the care of patients, you will also have an opportunity to increase your skills in working with people—how to respond to "demanding" patients, how to "bring out" uncommunicative patients, etc.

## RECORDING THE OBSERVATION

Since we already have covered the possibility of using mechanical aids in recording, this discussion will be confined to the manual recording of observational data by the observer.

### When Should Observations Be Recorded?

This should be done as close to the actual occurrence as possible. If notes are taken during the nurse-patient interaction, this should be explained to the patient, as indicated previously. The nurse who plans to "do all the patients" first and then "write all the notes" may find herself ascribing to Mrs. T. something which Mrs. W. really said, or forgetting entirely to record a very pertinent fact about Mr. L. The dangers of forgetting and/or actual misrecording due to interference of other events are ever-present and need to be minimized by making the time-lapse between observed event and recording as small as possible.

### What Should Be Recorded?

In general, the observer should record *at least*

what happened in the situation; this should include a description of the setting in which the observation took place, the name and the position of the observer, and an objective account of what was said and done by the interacting subjects. For example, most of your situations would involve interactions between nurse and patient, nurse and nurse, nurse and doctor, etc. In addition to these items the observer may, if he wishes, include subjective comments about his own feelings within the situation and his inferences about his own and/or the subject's motivations, value judgments, recommendations, etc. It is a good idea to keep the observational data separate from the observer's inferences and/or recommendations, so that if another person's interpretation is sought, this second person's judgment will not be influenced by reading what the first person thought about the data. (This is especially important in the case of patients who are mentally ill.)

### How Should This Be Recorded?

The basic guide here is to remember the purpose for the observation. Usually, in your situation, it will be in terms of a nursing care plan carried on with and for a patient. However, since you will not be the only person involved in giving this care, you must be able to communicate your pertinent observations to the next nurse in such a way that the words you use will mean the same things to her as they do to you. That this presents somewhat of a problem can be illustrated quite easily.

Let us leave the hospital situation temporarily and consider how we use some of the terms denoting frequency, like "always," "frequently," "sometimes," "as often as not," "rarely," and "never." Surely "always" means *always* and "never" means *never,* but do they? Have you ever said things like, "She's never on time!" or, "She always looks as if she came out of a bandbox!"? Now surely, if you think about it, the first "she" has been on time at least once in her life, even if you weren't around to see it; and the second "she" must surely wash her hair, and when it is dripping, can't possibly look "as if she came out of a bandbox." Moreover, if you try the following experiment on yourself and your friends, you will discover some very interesting (and enlightening) things about what these terms denoting frequency mean to different people. Ask 5 of your friends to write the terms "always," "frequently," etc., on a piece of paper, and then, next to each one, indicate the percentage of the time that a thing would have to happen, in order for them to say it "always" happened, it "frequently" happened, etc. Before you try this on your first friend, record your own responses.

We have tried this many times with both undergraduate and graduate groups and have found that they are consistent only in their response to "as often as not" which to most people means "50 per cent of the time." The responses to the other terms varied so widely that one participant in the experiment was prompted to remark that apparently "always sometimes meant frequently to some people, although it might also rarely mean never"! Therefore, instead of using these terms, it would be better to indicate the number of times or the percentage of the time that something occurred, as for example, "Patient asked to see the doctor 6 times during my half-hour with her" rather than "Patient frequently asked to see the doctor."

Another area in which we have some difficulty in communicating our ideas is in the area of "label-pasting." You might run across "pt. co-operative" or "pt. responded well to treatment." Let us examine these two labels "co-operative" and "responded well to treatment" a bit more critically. If a patient on complete bed-rest wished to wash her own face, and persisted in this wish, she would probably be labeled "un-co-operative"; if an ambulatory patient insisted that the nurse wash her face for her, she also would probably be labeled "un-co-operative." If all we know about these 2 patients is that they are both "un-co-operative," who knows what ideas we might get about their behavior?

Now let us look at this from another point of view. Nurse A gives Mrs. X a treatment, observes the latter's physical signs, and records "responded well to treatment" solely on the basis of her own opinions, although these are based on technical observational data. Nurse B gives Mrs. X the next treatment, observes the latter's physical signs, and asks, "How do you feel now, Mrs. X?" Mrs. X says, "Oh, so much better, Nurse. Not like the last time. I feel I can really go to sleep now." Nurse B also records "responded well to treatment." Nurse C comes into the situation and sees two separate recordings of "responded well to treatment," and so is totally unprepared for the patient's comment, "I hope this one will turn out like the one Miss B gave me, and not like Miss A's."

If Nurse A had recorded the patient's physical signs, and then her own opinion, "I think patient responded well to treatment," and if Nurse B had recorded the patient's physical signs together with the patient's comments, "patient says she feels

OBSERVATIONAL RECORD

| Observer ____________ | Date ____________ |
|---|---|
| Patient ____________ | Time ____________ |

Purpose for observation

Setting for observation

Data

| Interpretation | O do not write here |
|---|---|
| Recommendations | O do not write here |

much better than after last treatment—feels she can sleep now," and then her own opinion, "I think patient responded well to treatment," Nurse C might not have been caught out quite so flat-footedly!

These labels are really judgments made by the observer and are thus once removed from the observational data. These latter are sometimes omitted entirely in the mistaken notion that this saves time. It does, indeed, but to the detriment of intelligible communication. Even a brief outline of what is said and done is better than an ambiguous subjective label.

#### Suggested Format For Recording Observations

The form suggested on page 100 is based on the idea that two equally competent specialists analyzing the same set of observational data should come out with similar interpretations and/or recommendations. In order not to contaminate the thinking of any analysts who work with the data after the observer has recorded them, data should be kept physically separate from the observer's feelings and interpretations. Also, there should be space for any comments which the analysts wish to make.

### CHECKING THE OBSERVATIONAL DATA

Previously we mentioned that you will probably have occasion to refer to your ward instructor to check on both the validity and the accuracy of your observations. Previous notations by doctors and nurse-personnel should help, as well. If you have a record of observations previously made over a considerable time-period, and a noticeable pattern is evolving, a departure from the expected pattern should make you pause and question your data. Also, anything which looks "too good to be true" should be examined with greater care.

### FORMULATING THE ACTION-PLAN

When you are satisfied that the observational data are valid and reliable within the limits of human observers, the data may be used as a basis for future action. The purpose for collecting the data (i.e., for making the observations) indicates the type of action-plan which is desired as an outcome. For most of your work, it will be either to continue with the nursing-care plan presently in operation with and for a particular patient, or an alteration of the plan based on the data. If a change is to be made, be sure that you follow correct channels for instituting such a change. Your ward instructor, and a knowledge of hospital policy, should be helpful to you here.

# 9

# Writing Nursing Care Reports

The written report prepared most frequently by the student nurse is the nursing care study. The nursing student may be required to do at least one nursing care study on each major service: medical, surgical, obstetrics, pediatrics and psychiatry. Some schools of nursing have a form outline which students must follow; in others the student develops her own outline and prepares the material in the way she can best convey information.

The purposes of the nursing care study are to give the student experience in:

1. Preparing a paper which requires research in scientific literature
2. Pulling together scientific facts and demonstrating how this material is used in planning and giving patient care
3. Acquiring skill in written communication and
4. Developing a comprehensive study of a patient (based on observation and other data), for whom she has cared.

TREAT MENT
BACK GROUND
HISTORY
PRESENT ILLNESS
HISTORY

The following outline provides for the inclusion of the kinds of data pertinent in developing a nursing care study. It can be used if the student is planning to prepare an essay or if she plans to present the information in a short, concise outline.

Personal History

1. A. Socioeconomic-cultural Background

a. Include way in which this may have figured in the development of, or the course of present illness.

b. Include way in which this particular background has developed in the patient a set of values pertaining to health.

B. Family History

a. Include general health of other family members

b. Include past health status of patient

C. Present Illness

a. Compare
- (1) Normal function
- (2) Classical symptoms
- (3) Symptoms as presented by patient

D. Treatment Patient is Receiving

a. Include
- (1) Medicines
- (2) Diet
- (3) Special procedures
- (4) Tests and X-rays

E. Problems encountered in giving Nursing Care, and Steps Taken to Solve Them

a. Patient might have been able to turn on one side only

F. Rehabilitation
  a. Include
    (1) Physical
    (2) Psychological
    (3) Socio-economic
  b. Steps taken to further rehabilitation

Another kind of written report a nurse always uses is the "nurse's note." The nurse's note is a record of her observation of the patient. This serves as a form of communication between nurse and doctor and other members of the health team. It also serves as a communication to other nurses who are planning and giving care to this patient. The nurse's note is also a part of the permanent record of the patient.

Incidentally, many hospitals require that the nurse's note be printed. So if you do not print well, it would be worth your while to spend some time each day practicing by printing a paragraph from a newspaper or magazine, or something from your notes on reading material. It may save you time you would rather have for study, after admission to a school of nursing.

Whatever kind of a report you are preparing in the course of learning to be a nurse, you will be required to do two things:

1. to learn, use and spell correctly a new technical vocabulary, and
2. to describe exactly what you have observed, avoiding generalizations.

## NURSING CARE STUDY

We can take as an example a possible introductory statement to a nursing-care plan, or a note a nurse might make on a patient being admitted to a hospital. Refer to Chapter 8, "Making the Observation," "Recording the Observation."

Mrs. R. was admitted to the female medical floor via wheelchair. The admitting physician had made the diagnosis of rheumatic heart disease with mitral stenosis; mild congestive failure. Mrs. R. was a thin, frail-appearing Puerto Rican woman who appeared older than her 24 years of age. Observation of Mrs. R. revealed a slight cyanosis of her lips and nail beds. She was dyspneic; her respiration was 28, her pulse was 116, of good quality. but irregular. Her ankles were edematous, and there was some puffiness under her eyes.

An admission note made by the nurse on this same patient would include all of the pertinent information about the patient, but it would not be written in complete sentences.

"Thin, Puerto Rican female, admitted to female medical floor via wheelchair. Slight cyanosis of lips and nail beds; dyspneic; respiration 28, pulse 116—good quality, irregular. Edema of ankles, puffiness present under eyes. Patient says she has gained 12 pounds in past 2 weeks."

Much of the material the nurse writes is factual material based on careful observation and may be used to plan therapy for the patient. Precise reading is therefore important; the principles set forth in Chapter 8, "Characteristics of a Good Observation," apply here. When recording a patient's complaint of pain, it is important that the nurse be as descriptive as possible. Compare the following two statements:

1. "Patient complained of pain in chest."

2. "Patient complained of a 'crushing' pain in left anterior chest, some pain radiating down left arm."

Note that in the second statement the nurse has told exactly where the patient has pain, has quoted the patient as to what the pain is like (and many times this is of *utmost* importance), and has supplied the further information that the pain is not confined to the chest. The kind of note most useful to the doctor goes on to describe the appearance and behavior of the patient. To continue the second note above:

"Patient pale; some evidence of cyanosis; appears apprehensive; does not want to be left alone."

When writing a report or a nurse's note, you need to give thought to the choice of words. Refer again to Chapter 8, "How Should This Be Recorded?" Using this material, you recognize that "large amount," "moderate amount," "scant" may mean different things to different people. If you are attempting to measure drainage of some type, let us say, it is more meaningful to be as accurate and descriptive as possible. Note the number of dressings soaked with drainage; for instance, "4 large abdominal pads saturated in 1 hour."

Perhaps it is possible to measure the drainage. The amount of drainage and the time element are significant. The statement, "500 cc. of drainage in ½ hour," can be evaluated easily by the doctor.

The nursing care study should give evidence that you understood the nature of the patient's illness and its effect upon him. You should demonstrate the use of basic scientific facts in the plan for nursing care. One effective way to do this is by the use of an outline like the following which has been partially filled out in a schematic manner.

SURGICAL NURSING CARE STUDY

| Normal Function | Interference with Normal Function | Nursing Care Given |
|---|---|---|
| (Anatomy) The gall-bladder serves as a reservoir for the bile. It connects with the duodenum<br><br>(Physiology) During digestion, the gall-bladder is probably stimulated by acid-chyme to release bile into the duodenum.<br><br>(Chemistry) Bile is necessary for the emulsification of fats. | Stone in Common Bile Duct. Bile unable to pass through Common Bile Duct into duodenum. Presence of stone in Common Bile Duct has set up inflammatory process in gallbladder.<br><br>Mrs. F.P. unable to properly digest fats. | Mrs. F.P. has pain in right upper quadrant. Positioned in semi-Fowlers position for maximum comfort. *Demerol, 75 mg. given intramuscularly for relief of pain, every 3 hours as necessary.<br><br>Mrs. F.P. had temperature of 101°. Given fluids as tolerated in form of tea, fruit juice and water. When she was too nauseated to tolerate a sufficient amount of fluids by mouth, intravenous fluids were supplied. |

TREASURE MAP
TITLE
OUTLINE
LIBRARY
BURIED TREASURE
PREPARATION for LIBRARY WORK
J. McC.

# 10

# Writing Reports Based on Library Sources

It is entirely possible that one or more of your instructors will require you to submit a term paper or a written report for which you will be expected to trace library sources of information, as for example, in historical and/or ethical foundations of nursing. If you continue your academic preparation beyond the basic program, it is inevitable that you will be asked to prepare such reports. If you lack library, reading and note-taking skills, no amount of fancy writing will disguise the poor foundation on which your paper is based. It is the purpose of this chapter to make suggestions about ways in which the writing of reports of this type can be made systematic and quite rewarding in terms of the time and effort expended.

## MAKING AN OUTLINE

### Getting a Title

If an instructor requires the submission of a report based on library sources, there are three possibilities: (1) the title may be given by the instructor, in which case you have only to develop it; (2) the instructor may mention several main areas and leave it to you to pinpoint your special interest in any one area; or (3) the instructor may leave the whole thing up to you, specifying only that the paper have some bearing on what you are studying in the course.

In order to make our discussion more specific, let us suppose that we are dealing with the third possibility, in a course in foundations of nursing. Let us suppose further that our interest has been piqued by the fact that only about 50 years ago blood pressure was not taken routinely on the wards for postoperative patients, that diabetes was a dreaded and disabling disease, and that typhoid fever was a fairly common occurrence, especially in certain localities. So far, this is just the glimmering of an idea. However, let us pursue it further. We know that medical knowledge, and therefore nursing knowledge, was augmented considerably whenever a national emergency arose. We know also that in order to get revealing contrasts in historical research a period of 100 years is likely to be rewarding. We might make our idea more specific then by considering "changes since 1860," thus bringing in the Civil War, the Spanish-American War, and two World Wars, among other national emergencies.

The next question is, "changes in what?" Why do we take the postoperative patient's blood pressure regularly until it becomes stabilized now, when we did not do so at the turn of the century? Today most diabetics are taught to control their disease, and unless complications set in, can take their places in society without much ado. How did this happen? If we experience a typhoid epidemic now, this is a relatively rare occurrence and likely to be regarded as a blot on society's escutcheon. Why? We can identify these "changes" so far as: (1) changes in presenting health problems;* (2) changes in nursing practice and (3) changes in medicine. Since we are primarily interested in nursing practice, we might try a tentative title linking (1) and (2) together, thus: "Changes in Presenting Health Problems Since 1860, and Their Reflection in Nursing Practice."

If we let this title stand, we must be prepared to cope with two consequences: (1) we shall have to study every country in the world from 1860 on; and (2) we shall have to locate every single change in presenting health problems which occurred since 1860! Let us hasten to delimit the area of our investigations by qualifying the title to read, "Some Changes in Presenting Health Problems in the USA Since 1860, and Their Reflection in Nursing Practice." At this point it might occur to us that "reflection in" could be replaced by "effect on" to further clarify the idea. However, now we are saying that we shall show direct cause-and-effect relationship between a change in a presenting health problem and a change in a particular nursing practice. Since it is likely that some, if not all, of our sources will provide hearsay rather than primary evidence (since we shall not be able to get the sworn depositions of the people who were responsible for the changes in nursing practice), we had better qualify further by including the word "probable" in the title, as follows: "Some

* A "presenting health problem" is one that has been identified.

Changes in Presenting Health Problems in the United States Since 1860, and Their Probable Effect on Nursing Practice."

## Developing the Outline

We might begin by asking ourselves why presenting health problems change? Wars, epidemics —these are social conditions. Then, too, we have scientific discoveries which might conquer a particular health problem so that it practically disappears, as for example, our tremendous strides forward in reducing such contagious diseases as smallpox and scarlet fever, etc. The kinds of health services made available to the consumer have something to do with this question, too— the current facilities for chest X-ray in our campaign against tuberculosis of the lungs, for example. We might then begin our outline with a main heading "Factors influencing presenting health problems," with subheadings "Social conditions," "Scientific discoveries," and "Available health services." We might next consider what areas of nursing practice we want to focus upon, since we have said in our title that we would look only at *some* changes in presenting health problems. With the tremendous emphasis that is being placed at the present time on health teaching and on the idea of preventing disease conditions as well as curing them, we are concerned with people both in and out of hospitals; therefore, we are concerned with both hospital and public health nursing. Also, somewhere in this development we need to recognize the growing importance of pediatric and psychiatric nursing.

Let us now try to put these various ideas together into the first rough working outline.

Some Changes in Presenting Health Problems in the USA Since 1860, and Their Probable Effect on Nursing Practice

I. Factors influencing presenting health problems
    A. Social conditions
    B. Scientific discoveries
    C. Available health services

II. Areas of nursing practice reflecting changes
    A. Hospital nursing
        1. Pediatric nursing
        2. Psychiatric nursing
    B. Public Health nursing

This is only one possible outline which might be worked out from the given title, and of course, it might have been arrived at by mental processes other than the ones detailed here. It is presented merely as an example.

Let us assume, then, that a rough working outline on some topic has been established, and that we are ready for the next step, which is that of locating pertinent information.

## WHAT ARE THE LIKELIEST SOURCES OF INFORMATION?

Among the possibilities are books, periodicals, newspapers, pamphlets, and unpublished materials of various kinds (e.g., mimeographed, privately printed and circulated, etc.). If your coverage is to be thorough, it is well to consider all these sources and to establish a time limit for the search. For example, you may wish to review the literature in a certain area from 1940 to 1950. At first glance, this seems perfectly clear. However, do you mean "January 1, 1940, to January 1, 1950," or "January 1, 1940, to December 31, 1950?" That is, are both dates inclusive, or not? Then, having made this decision, do you mean "published" between these dates, "submitted for publication" between these dates, or actually "written" between these dates? Of these three possibilities the first one, i.e., "published," is the easiest to locate because as a general rule books, periodicals, etc. bear the date of publication. However, many of the periodicals are behind in their printing schedules, and when this is the case, the article usually contains a footnote giving the date on which it was submitted. Knowledge of this fact becomes of paramount importance if you wish to trace the literature back 5 years from the current issues, say, and your chief interest is to get the up-to-the-minute reports. It might make quite a difference in certain areas of research to know that the latest study "hot off the press" was submitted 2 years ago! If we realize that the study took some time to make and to report, we conclude sadly that the materials presented are *more* than 2 years old.

In tracing the literature it is a good idea to start with the most recent date in which you are interested and work backward, rather than to begin with the oldest publication and work forward. The reason for this is the possible economy of time that will occur if the investigators who are reporting are as co-operative as we hope they will be. Most reputable researchers include up-to-the-minute bibliographies in their reports, and these may save time in the location and/or summary of pertinent information. For example, it is quite likely that for the outline presented, you will get a greater return on your investment of time if you start with the most recently published history of nursing, rather than with some of the "old classics."

**Books**

Books can be located according to topic in the card index of your school or public library. Each card contains items such as the name of the author, the title, the name of the publisher, the place of publication, the date of copyright and/or the date of publication, and it may also give an annotation dealing with the contents of the book. However, if you rely on the card index alone to provide you with a list of pertinent books, you are assuming that your library owns all pertinent published books in your area of interest, and this may not be the case.

Thus if you have browsed the library without coming up with what you seek, you may find some of the references in the following guide worth browsing:

A. IF YOU DON'T KNOW IF THE BOOK IS IN PRINT OR OUT OF PRINT—consult the *Cumulative Book Index.** This contains a list of books in the English language published throughout the world, catalogued by author, title and subject in one alphabetical list. It is bound in 2 volumes per year, January to July and August to December. It is also bound in 2-year and 5-year accumulations. Thus it is handy for locating all books by any one author or in any one particular subject which appeared in a given time span.

B. IF IT IS IN PRINT—the book will be listed in *Books in Print.** Since this lists all books twice —by author, and then again by title, you need know only either factor. And since these titles are

* These references are available in public libraries and in well-stocked bookstores.

in print, they are available through the bookstore and the publisher as well as the library. The publisher for each publication is identified in both the *Cumulative Book Index* and *Books In Print*.

*When the Publisher Is Known*—another reference may help. The *Trade List Annual** lists books in print according to publisher. Some of the lists carry short descriptions of each book and this may save time in selecting only what you actually will be able to use.

C. IF IT IS NOT IN PRINT—the book will not appear in an up-to-date issue of *Books In Print;* with information from the *Cumulative Book Index,* you can consult secondhand book stores if the local library does not carry the title.

D. IF YOU DO NOT KNOW EITHER AUTHOR OR TITLE—there are 3 references that may help:

1. *Cumulative Book Index*. As mentioned, this lists books by subject as well as by author and title. Thus, if you look up nursing in the volume for August-December, 1957, you will find a major heading "Nurses and nursing," and under that the subheads "Dictionaries and encyclopedias," "History" and "Statistics." Following these is another major heading, "Nurses and nursing, Public health."

2. *Subject Guide to Books in Print*.* This annual index is just what it says it is. It covers many fields, and under "Nursing" it has 9 subheads. Use it in conjunction with *Books in Print*.

3. *Bibliographies on Nursing,* available from the National League for Nursing, cover the health fields (see page 120).

* These references are available in public libraries and in well-stocked bookstores.

E. IF YOU KNOW WHAT YOU WANT BUT CAN'T FIND A COPY, there are two last resorts. Assuming that the local libraries and bookstores and the publisher can't provide the volume, you can

1. Ask the local library or bookstore for names of large secondhand book stores in other cities, and write to them, or

2. Telephone or write the regional Union Library Catalogue. This is a service subscribed to largely by teaching institutions for use by students and instructors. There are 4 regional offices that perform a precise function: they keep a record of all books in most, and sometimes all, of the libraries in their region, and thus can tell you where to find a particular title. The Union Library Catalogue in Philadelphia covers libraries in Eastern Pennsylvania; in Cleveland the local office covers just Cleveland; the Denver office includes Colorado, Wyoming and parts of surrounding states; and the Seattle office has scouted the Pacific Northwest.

### Periodicals

In the area of periodicals we have, in some of the specialized fields, a number of guides and indexes, and abstracts and summaries as well. At the front of each guide or index there appears a list of the periodicals indexed therein. The *Reader's Guide to Periodical Literature* contains an author and subject index; so also does the *Education Index* and the *Index Medicus*. In specialized fields we have such bibliographic aids as the *Psychological Abstracts,* which aims to include all articles written, including those not in English;

and the *Review of Educational Research,* which cyclically collates all the research done in a particular area. For example, the December, 1953, issue deals with "The Education of Exceptional Children" and we are told in the foreword that,

> The first five chapters of this review cover the literature on various types of exceptional children for a nine-year period. The final two chapters treat of research pertaining to the visually handicapped and the orthopedically handicapped for the 12-year period from June, 1941, to June, 1953.

In the nursing area, both the *American Journal of Nursing* and *Nursing Outlook* have annotated bibliography cards for all their articles, and may be purchased on a subscription basis. The National League for Nursing, 2 Park Avenue, New York, N. Y., offers a series of bibliographies on nursing publications. At present there are 14 of these paper-bound manuals, each covering a small segment of the field. For instance, volume 8 ($2.50), covers surgical nursing, cancer nursing, communicable disease nursing and geriatric nursing. In most cases the listings in each manual are broken down into "Books" and "Articles and Pamphlets."

### Serials, Newspapers, Etc.

We have the *Union List of Serials* and the *Union List of Newspapers,* indicating geographically where collections of specific serials and newspapers can be found, and what time-period is covered in each collection. There are also lists of Government publications and of thesis titles which are reportedly being written.

If you need a more fully detailed discussion,

two sources of help are available to you: (1) recently published books dealing with the location of bibliographic information and (2) your school librarian. The reason for putting them in this order is that any serious student should learn how to extend his skills through the bibliographic resources which are available; the librarian should be looked upon as a consultant, and not as a bibliographic nursemaid.

## SUGGESTED LIBRARY PROCEDURE

The procedure which will be suggested here is an outgrowth of the following considerations:

1. The nasty process of "copying over" should be minimized. There should be but a *single recording* during the process of going from the literature to the rough draft of the report. We should not have to copy from the source to our notes, and from our notes to the report in its various stages from rough to final form.

2. The note-taking system should be such as to allow for a systematic review of the literature, even if you can spend only a short period of time in any one session. You should not feel that it is "not worth your while" to go to the library for "so short a time."

3. The note-taking system should be such that full bibliographic citations are possible for any reading notes which you want to incorporate into your report.

4. The note-taking system should be sufficiently flexible so that no recopying of reading notes needs to be done, if the working outline for the paper or report is changed. (This presupposes

the smallest possible meaningful unit of recording.)

The following suggestions will include procedures for locating sources and making a reading priority list, reading and note-taking, and collating reading notes and incorporating them into your report. They are the outcome of the findings and suggestions of many authorities in the field of bibliographic technic. However, remember again that they may have to be adapted to your personal needs.

### Suggestions for Organization

Before you make your first trip to the library to locate source materials, let us think a bit about getting organized for action, using the outline we have previously developed as an illustration. The system given below is based on the foregoing considerations.

1. Provide yourself with the following items: a manila or other envelope for filing 3-inch by 5-inch cards, and pads of paper for use in reading sessions; a cardboard or other box-file of the same size for collating the notes made in each reading session; some sets of differently colored tabulation cards of the 3-inch by 5-inch size to act as dividers in both the envelope and box-files (the number of different colors you will need depends on the number of kinds of headings you have used in your outline; we have used three: main, sub, and sub-sub); some 3-inch by 5-inch pads of (white) paper on which to make the actual reading notes; and some 8½-inch by 11-inch paper cut into 1-inch strips lengthwise (discarded notebook sheets already used on one side or yellow

scratch paper will do very well for this) to use as markers in reading.

2. Let us assume that you have selected blue, salmon and yellow as the colors for the dividers—blue for main headings in the outline, salmon for subheadings and yellow for subsubheadings. Prepare duplicate sets of cards by writing the key words (or the entire heading if possible) on the tabs of the cards as illustrated:

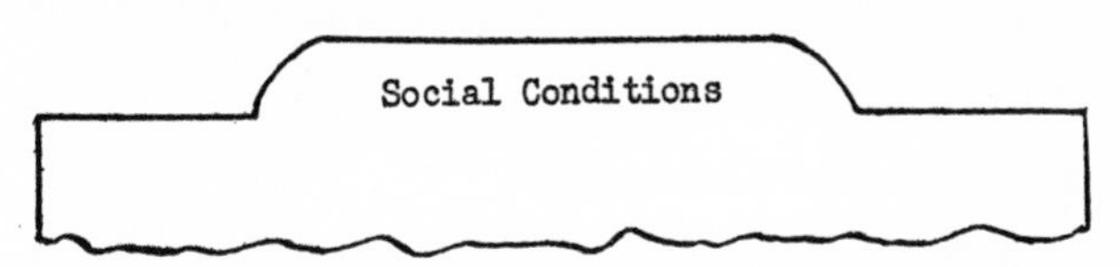


3. Arrange these two sets of cards in sequence according to your outline in each file, including a few blank cards of each color in case you find it necessary to expand or change your outline.

4. Prepare duplicate (blue) cards labeled "Bibliography—Possible," "Bibliography—Usable," and "Bibliography—Not Usable," and place a set in front of the outline sets in each file.

5. Take to the library your manila envelope file, the pads of 3-inch by 5-inch paper, and the 1-inch strips. How large a supply to take with you for each session will become clearer as we follow through the rest of the suggested procedure.

### Suggestions for Making a Reading Priority List

Books and periodicals are likely to be our best sources of information. Therefore, let us consult the *Cumulative Book Index* under "Nursing," and as a start, go back from the current issue for 10 years. There is nothing sacred about 10; it is simply the time limit for our first fishing expedition to see what we come up with. If the "catch" is meager, we can go back 15, 20, or whatever number of years we need. On the top sheet of one of our 3-inch by 5-inch pads, we make a heading "Cumulative Book Index" and record each volume traced. (If you leave the sheet attached until you have completed it, you will find it easier to handle. Detached sheets have a way of eluding you when you want them!)

Let us suppose that for March, 1957, we locate the book* *Changes in Nursing Practice for the Past Fifty Years* by Dale Arden, published by B. Crosby, Co., in New Orleans. This certainly looks like a good possibility! On the top sheet of another 3-inch by 5-inch pad we record the complete bibliographic citation as follows:

```
Arden, Dale

Changes in Nursing Practice for the Past
  Fifty Years

New Orleans, La., B. Crosby Co.
1957
```

This sheet is filed behind "Bibliography—Possible." In the same way, we make out a sheet for each likely book and record on the "Cumulative Book Index" sheet each volume traced, going back 10 years.

In regard to periodicals, with a topic like the illustration, the nursing literature would be a good starting place—we might consult the cumu-

* All references which follow are fictitious.

lative indexes for the *American Journal of Nursing, Nursing Outlook,* and *Nursing Research.* When a year's issue of these journals are bound together in one volume, the indexes are usually found within, either at the very front or in the back. However, it should be noted that since our paper deals with social conditions, scientific discoveries, etc., it is entirely possible that we shall want to augment the nursing literature with that from other fields, for both books and periodicals. This decision might be made later, after the nursing literature has been reviewed and we have asked ourselves whether we are content with the coverage which has been provided, in terms of how we wish to develop our report.

Suppose that in the *American Journal of Nursing,* Volume 46, for October, 1956, we find an article by Verna Joly entitled Psychiatric nursing looks back to 1900, on pages 947 to 952, which looks promising. The tracing sheet has now been headed "AJN" and the volumes traced are being recorded in sequence. The bibliography sheet is now filled out as follows:

> Joly, Verna
>
> "Psychiatric Nursing Looks Back to 1900"
>
> Amer J Nurs 46: 947 - 952, Oct., 1956

Again, this sheet is filed behind "Bibliography—Possible." In the same way, a sheet is made out for each likely article until guides and indexes have yielded all possible leads back through the same span to be traced.

We are now ready to begin to read. The question is, in what order shall we tackle the sheets filed behind "Bibliography—Possible"? Recalling now our hope that the authors will have done a good review of the literature which they will pass on to us in capsule form, we arrange the sheets chronologically by date of publication, with the most recent one on top. Then, depending on the period of time available and our reading speed, we decide what to tackle in a given session. In our illustration, Arden's book is first, followed by Joly's article. We try the book first, since it is possible that the article may be covered therein.

### Suggestions for Reading and Note-Taking

The table of contents should tell us which chapters are of particular importance, and we note these on the Arden sheet which we have taken from behind "Bibliography—Possible" and numbered "1" in the upper right hand corner to indicate that it is the first reference being read.

Mindful of the fact that we want to take two kinds of reading notes: (1) summaries of author's ideas in our own words and (2) direct quotations as authority for our later statements, we read the chapter summary first if there is one, and then section and/or paragraph headings to help us with our frame of reference (see also chapter on "Becoming a More Efficient Reader"). This will help us to anticipate the author and read more rapidly. Now we begin to read paragraph by paragraph. Let us suppose that halfway down the first page we come upon a couple of sentences which are such gems that we want them for our collection. However, instead of copying anything yet, we take one of our strips of (yellow) paper, line it up with the bottom of the page, and mark the beginning and end of the passage we want to copy, thus:

We leave the slip in the appropriate page, numbering it to avoid later confusion, and continue reading. It is quite possible that two pages hence the author will condense these ideas into one pithy sentence, in which case we mark the new sentence similarly and remove and destroy the first marker. In this way we read the entire chapter, marking those gems which we wish to copy verbatim, as well as those passages whose ideas we wish to summarize. (In the latter case, a word or two to cue you may be written on the marker for ease in later summarization.)

We are now ready to make our reading notes. Suppose that on page 47 of Arden's book we have marked a sentence for direct quotation, possibly referring to what doctors and nurses learned during the Civil War about the treatment of amputees. We make this note on a 3-inch by 5-inch sheet as follows:

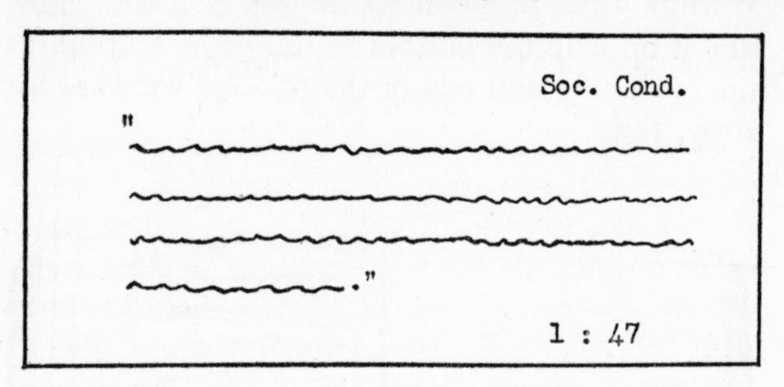


Note the quotation marks indicating a direct quote: the code "Soc. Cond." in the upper right-hand corner, indicating that this reading note is to be filed (at least temporarily) behind what we have called "Social Conditions" under the main outline heading "Factors Influencing Presenting Health Problems"; and the numbers "1 : 47" in the lower right-hand corner. The "1" indicates that the note comes from reference number 1, which is the Arden book, since it is the first to be read (note the "1" on the corresponding bibliography sheet), and the "47" following the colon, which indicates the page number.

If we had marked a paragraph for summary in our own words, the same type of reading note would have been made, omitting the quotation marks. At the end of the chapter, we file all the notes for that chapter behind their appropriate tabulation cards in our manila envelope and proceed to the next chapter. Suppose that our time runs out halfway through a chapter, before we have had a chance to make our notes. At this point we simply pull out our (yellow) markers which have page numbers recorded on them, clip them to the Arden bibliography sheet, surrender the book, and go off to class. It is an easy matter to reinsert them at our next session with this book.

As we go along, we may find ourselves getting ideas of our own about what is going on. In this case, it has been found helpful to use red or some other distinctive color to record the opinion right on the reading note, or, if it is not directly pertinent to the note, to record it for further consideration on a separate sheet to be filed behind the appropriate outline card. Bright ideas on how to develop the report, neat ways of saying things, etc., can be preserved easily in this way.

When a reference has been completed, its bibliography sheet is filed behind "Bibliography—Usable." As references are read (presumably in the chronological order of their publication, beginning with the most recent, as we have discussed), those which do not live up to their earlier promise of usefulness are filed behind "Bibliography—Not Usable." Those references which make a contribution are numbered in sequence in the order in which they are read, and these numbers provide the link between the reference and the reading notes taken from it. For example, if the Joly article is read next, it would be numbered "2" and all reading notes taken from it would be coded with a "2," a colon and a page number.

### Collating Reading Notes

At the end of each reading session it is a good idea to transfer the reading notes from the envelope file to the box file. At this time, a glance at each note to see whether you still agree with the heading under which you propose to file it will help you to decide whether or not additional headings are required. Also, it is well, at strategic intervals, to glance over the accumulated reading notes for a given heading in the box file, and to clip together those noted as dealing with the same point. In this way, if 6 authors have mentioned a point, and 4 hold one opinion while 2 hold another, this will be brought to your attention so that additional evidence on this point can be sought in subsequent references.

## INCORPORATING READING NOTES INTO THE REPORT

### Arranging the Notes

When all the sources have been reviewed and our file of reading notes is complete, we are ready to begin on the first draft of the report. The notes behind the card for the first outline topic or heading are taken out of the box file and spread on a flat surface (large table or the floor, depending on the volume of the cards), and arranged so that they come in a meaningful sequence in terms of the development of the report. At this point some notes may be discarded, or refiled behind another heading card as being more pertinent to the latter topic. It has been found helpful to pin this tentative final arrangement of notes to a large sheet of wrapping or other paper. It is a good idea to proceed in like manner with the notes for the rest of the headings before actually beginning to write, since it is as likely that notes will be moved ahead as back, and it is better to wait until all the notes have been at least tentatively organized.

### Incorporating the Notes

Now comes the actual writing process. We begin to develop the first topic and decide to use the first reading note as a direct quotation. The note is unpinned from its place on the wrapping paper, and repinned in its proper place on our manuscript page. Reading notes which contain summaries in our own words are treated in similar fashion. When we come upon several notes dealing with the same point, we summarize these in the manuscript in our own words, pin the notes together over the place on the page where we have made our summary, and leave space on the page for including the proper citation of references later. This is shown in the illustration.

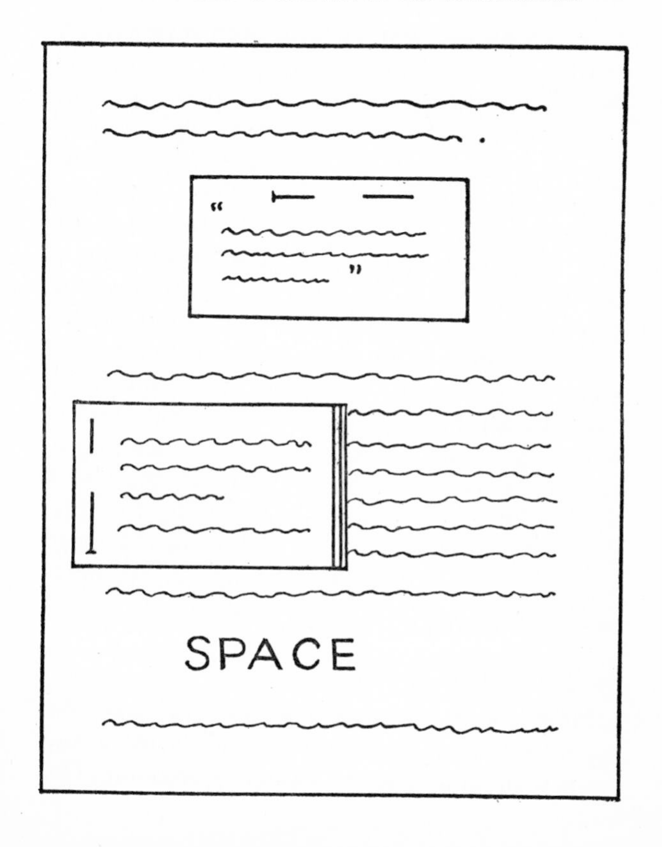

We continue until we have finished with the first topic. If any reading notes remain, either they are incorporated or discarded. It is suggested that the ones to be discarded be left pinned to the wrapping paper until the final draft of the manuscript is completed.

All the topics in the outline are treated in similar fashion. If more than one rough draft of the manuscript is necessary before the final typed form, the reading notes are transferred from draft to draft *without ever being copied.*

## ASSEMBLING THE BIBLIOGRAPHY

When the last rough draft of the manuscript is ready to go into the final typed form, correct citations for all reading noted must appear in the text, and a bibliography must be assembled. We now go through the reading notes in the manuscript and record the numbers of the references from which they come (the numbers to the left of the colon on each note). Then we go to the file and remove the bibliography sheets having *these same numbers* in the upper right-hand corner. These sheets should come from the "Bibliography—Usable" category.

Let us recall now that these sheets have been numbered in the order in which the references were read, which is based on the chronological order of publication, beginning with the most recent. Also, let us recall that bibliographies are arranged in *alphabetical* order. Therefore, we arrange the selected sheets in the alphabetical order of the authors' last names and renumber them beginning with "1" right under the previous number in the upper right-hand corner, which we had circled. (You may prefer to use another color for these alphabetical numbers.) For example, suppose that the first sheet in the alphabetical file is for an article by Hortense Ackley published in 1948, which was read as the 21st reference. This sheet would be renumbered as follows:

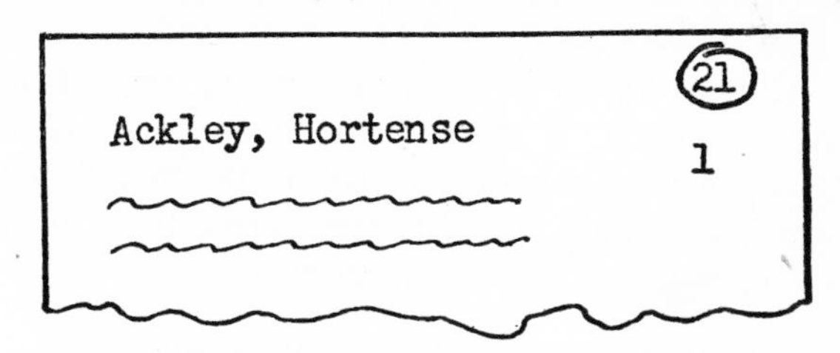


Let us further suppose that the second sheet in the alphabetical file belongs to the Arden reference, which we read first. This sheet would be renumbered as follows:

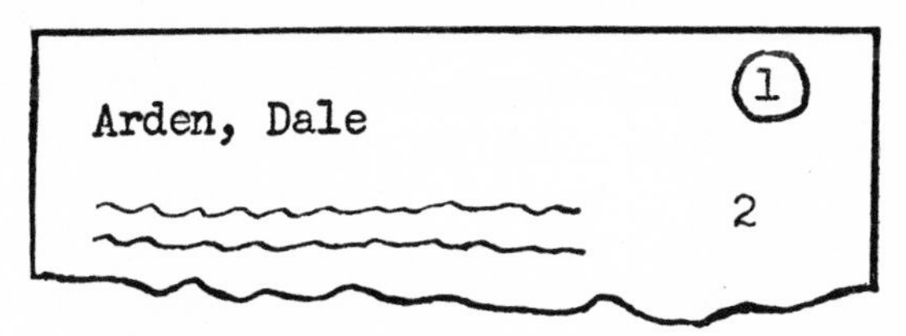


In the same way, all of the sheets in the alphabetical file are renumbered in sequence. The bibliography is then typed directly from these sheets, *numbering the references in alphabetical order as they appear in the upper right-hand corner*. If your instructor has indicated a style for bibliographic listings, it should be used here. If not, the style illustrated previously for books (Arden) and for periodicals (Joly) may be used. It is a good idea to make a note of the sources traced and the time-span covered in the bibliographic listing. This is easily done from the "tracing" sheets which were referred to under **Suggestions For Making a Reading Priority List.**

## CITING REFERENCES IN THE REPORT

The alphabetical numbers should now be recorded on the reading notes pinned to the final rough draft, so that when the manuscript is typed the citations will correspond with the bibliographic sequence. A simple and acceptable way (used by the American Educational Research Association) of indicating citations in the body of a report is to enclose the citation in parentheses, giving the alphabetical number of the reference first, followed by a colon and the page number or numbers, as in

( 17 : 430 )

If more than one citation is to be given, as for example, in the summary of four references, these may be offset by semicolons, as in

(17 : 430; 18 : 27; 21 : 26 to 38; 25 : 14 to 17)

The first appearance of this notation in the text should be starred and a footnote explanation of what the numbers represent should be given.

Just a word of caution here; it is a good idea to make a carbon of any written report which you submit, just in case the instructor wishes to keep the original for her files. You never know when it might come in handy in the future. And a second word of caution; don't destroy your final rough draft and/or your reading file until your report has been graded. After this, if you have made a carbon for yourself, it's fairly safe to celebrate with a bonfire!

# Epilogue

## New Worlds to Conquer!

# Appendix

## *Combining Forms and Prefixes*

These forms, with a prefix or a suffix, or both, are those most commonly used in making medical words. G indicates those from the Greek; L, those from the Latin. Properly, Greek forms should be used only with Greek prefixes and suffixes; Latin, with Latin. Often a vowel, usually a, i or o, is needed for euphony.

**A-** or **Ab-** (L) *away, lack of:* abnormal, departing from normal.
**A-** or **An-** (G) *from, without:* asepsis, without infection.
**Acr-** (G) *an extremity:* acrodermatitis, a dermatitis of the limbs.
**Ad-** (L) *to, toward, near:* adrenal, near the kidney.
**Aden-** (G) *gland:* adenitis, inflammation of a gland.
**Alg-** (G) *pain:* neuralgia, pain extending along nerves.
**Ambi-** (L) *both:* ambidextrous, referring to both hands.
**Ante-** (L) *before:* antenatal, occurring or having been formed before birth.
**Anti-** (G) *against:* antiseptic, against or preventing sepsis.
**Arth-** (G) *joint:* arthritis, inflammation of a joint.
**Auto-** (G) *self:* auto-intoxication, poisoning by toxin generated in the body.

**Bi-** or **Bin-** (L) *two:* binocular, pertaining to both eyes.
**Bio-** (G) *life:* biopsy, inspection of living organism (or tissue).
**Blast-** (G) *bud, a growing thing in early stages:* blastocyte, beginning cell not yet differentiated.
**Bleph-** (G) *eyelids:* blepharitis, inflammation of an eyelid.
**Brachi-** (G) *arm:* brachialis, muscle for flexing forearm.
**Brachy-** (G) *short:* brachydactylia, abnormal shortness of fingers and toes.
**Brady-** (G) *slow:* bradycardia, abnormal slowness of heartbeat.

**Bronch-** (G) *windpipe:* bronchiectasis, dilation of bronchial tubes.
**Bucc-** (L) *cheek:* buccally, toward the cheek.

**Carcin-** (G) *cancer:* carcinogenic, producing cancer.
**Cardi-** (G) *heart:* cardialgia, pain in the heart.
**Cephal-** (G) *head:* encephalitis, inflammation of brain.
**Cheil-** (G) *lip:* cheilitis, inflammation of the lip.
**Chole-** (G) *bile:* cholecyst, the gallbladder.
**Chondr-** (G) *cartilage:* chondrectomy, removal of a cartilage.
**Circum-** (L) *around:* circumocular, around the eyes.
**Cleid-** (G) *clavicle:* cleidocostal, pertaining to clavicle and ribs.
**Colp-** (G) *vagina:* colporrhagia, vaginal hemorrhage.
**Contra-** (L) *against, opposed:* contraindication, indication opposing usually indicated treatment.
**Cost-** (L) *rib:* intercostal, between the ribs.
**Counter-** (L) *against:* counterirritation, an irritation to relieve some other irritation (e.g., a liniment).
**Crani-** (L) *skull:* craniotomy, surgical opening in skull.
**Crypt-** (G) *hidden:* cryptogenic, of hidden or unknown origin.
**Cut-** (L) *skin:* subcutaneous, under the skin.
**Cyst-** (G) *sac or bladder:* cystitis, inflammation of the bladder.
**Cyto-** (G) *cell:* cytology, scientific study of cells; cytometer, a device for counting and measuring cells.

**Dacry-** (G) *lachrymal glands:* dacryocyst, tear-sac.
**Derm-** or **Dermat-** (G) *skin:* dermatoid, skinlike.
**Di-** (L) *two:* diphasic, occurring in two stages or phases.
**Dis-** (L) *apart:* disarticulation, taking joint apart.
**Dys-** (G) *pain or difficulty:* dyspepsia, impairment of digestion.

**Ecto-** (G) *outside:* ectoretina, outermost layer of retina.
**Em-** or **En-** (G) *in:* encapsulated, enclosed in a capsule.
**Encephal-** (G) *brain:* encephalitis, inflammation of brain.
**End-** (G) *within:* endothelium, layer of cells lining heart, blood and lymph vessels.
**Entero-** (G) *intestine:* enterosis, falling of intestine.
**Epi-** (G) *above or upon:* epidermis, outermost layer of skin.
**Erythro-** (G) *red:* erythrocyte, red blood cell.
**Eu-** (G) *well:* euphoria, well feeling, feeling of good health.

**Ex-** or **E-** (L) *out:* excretion, material thrown out of the body or the organ.

**Exo-** (G) *outside:* exocrine, excreting outwardly (opposite of endocrine).

**Extra-** (G) *outside:* extramural, situated or occurring outside a wall.

**Febri-** (L) *fever:* febrile, feverish.

**Galacto-** (G) *milk:* galactose, a milk-sugar.

**Gastr-** (G) *stomach:* gastrectomy, excision of the stomach.

**Gloss-** (G) *tongue:* glossectomy, surgical removal of tongue.

**Glyco-** (G) *sugar:* glycosuria, sugar in the urine.

**Gynec-** (G) *woman:* gynecology, science of diseases pertaining to women.

**Hem-** or **Hemat-** (G) *blood:* hemopoiesis, forming blood.

**Hemi-** (G) *half:* heminephrectomy, excision of half the kidney.

**Hepat-** (G) *liver:* hepatitis, inflammation of the liver.

**Hetero-** (G) *other* (opposite of homo): heterotransplant, using skin from a member of another species.

**Hist-** (G) *tissue:* histology, science of minute structure and function of tissues.

**Homo-** (G) *same:* homotransplant, skin grafting by using skin from a member of the same species.

**Hydr-** (G) *water:* hydrocephalus, abnormal accumulation of fluid in cranium.

**Hyper-** (G) *above, excess of:* hyperglycemia, excess of sugar in blood.

**Hypo-** (G) *under, deficiency of:* hypoglycemia, deficiency of sugar in blood.

**Hyster-** (G) *uterus:* hysterectomy, excision of uterus.

**Idio-** (G) *self, or separate:* idiopathic, a disease self-originated (of unknown cause).

**Im-** or **In-** (L) *in:* infiltration, accumulation in tissue of abnormal substances.

**Im-** or **In-** (L) *not:* immature, not mature.

**Infra-** (L) *below:* infra-orbital, below the orbit.

**Inter-** (L) *between:* intermuscular, between the muscles.

**Intra-** (L) *within:* intramuscular, within the muscle.

**Kerat-** (G) *horn, cornea:* keratitis, inflammation of cornea.

**Lact-** (L) *milk:* lactation, secretion of milk.
**Leuk-** (G) *white:* leukocyte, white cell.

**Macro-** (G) *large:* macroblast, abnormally large red cell.
**Mast-** (G) *breast:* mastectomy, excision of the breast.
**Meg-** or **Megal-** (G) *great:* megacolon, abnormally large colon.
**Ment-** (L) *mind:* dementia, deterioration of the mind.
**Mer-** (G) *part:* merotomy, division into segments.
**Mesa-** (G) *middle:* mesaortitis, inflammation of middle coat of the aorta.
**Meta-** (G) *beyond, over, change:* metastasis, change in seat of a disease.
**Micro-** (G) *small:* microplasia, dwarfism.
**My-** (G) *muscle:* myoma, tumor made of muscular elements.
**Myc-** (G) *fungi:* mycology, science and study of fungi.

**Necro-** (G) *corpse, dead:* necrosis, death of cells adjoining living tissue.
**Neo-** (G) *new:* neoplasm, any new growth or formation.
**Neph-** (G) *kidney:* nephrectomy, surgical excision of kidney.
**Neuro-** (G) *nerve:* neuron, nerve cell.

**Odont-** (G) *tooth:* odontology, dentistry.
**Olig-** (G) *little:* oligemia, deficiency in volume of blood.
**Oo-** (G) *egg:* oocyte, original cell of egg.
**Oophor-** (G) *ovary:* oophorectomy, removal of an ovary.
**Ophthalm-** (G) *eye:* ophthalmometer, an instrument for measuring the eye.
**Ortho-** (G) *straight, normal:* orthograde, walk straight (upright).
**Oss-** (L) *bone:* osseous, bony.
**Oste-** (G) *bone:* osteitis, inflammation of a bone.
**Ot-** (G) *ear:* otorrhea, discharge from ear.
**Ovar-** (G) *ovary:* ovariorrhexis, rupture of an ovary.

**Para-** (G) *irregular, around, wrong:* paradenitis, inflammation of tissue in the neighborhood of a gland.
**Path-** (G) *disease:* pathology, science of disease.
**Ped-**[1] (G) *children:* pediatrician, child specialist.
**Ped-**[2] (L) *feet:* pedograph, imprint of the foot.

[1] **Ped**—from Greek *pais,* child.
[2] **Ped**—from Latin *pes,* foot.

**Per-** (L) *through, excessively:* percutaneous, through the skin.

**Peri-** (G) *around, immediately around* (in contradistinction to para): periapical, surrounding apex of root of tooth.

**Phil-** (G) *love:* hemophilic, fond of blood (as bacteria that grow well in presence of hemoglobin).

**Phleb-** (G) *vein:* phlebotomy, opening of vein for bloodletting.

**Phob-** (G) *fear:* hydrophobic, reluctant to associate with water.

**Pneum-** or **Pneumon-** (G) *lung* (pneum—air): pneumococcus, organism causing lobar pneumonia.

**Polio-** (G) *gray:* poliomyelitis, inflammation of gray substance of spinal cord.

**Poly-** (G) *many:* polyarthritis, inflammation of several joints.

**Post-** (L) *after:* postpartum, after delivery.

**Pre-** (L) *before:* prenatal, occurring before birth.

**Pro-** (L and G) *before:* prognosis, forecast as to result of disease.

**Proct-** (G) *rectum:* proctectomy, surgical removal of rectum.

**Pseudo-** (G) *false:* pseudoangina, false angina.

**Psych-** (G) *soul or mind:* psychiatry, treatment of mental disorders.

**Py-** (G) *pus:* pyorrhea, discharge of pus.

**Pyel-** (G) *pelvis:* pyelitis, inflammation of pelvis of kidney.

**Rach-** (G) *spine:* rachicentesis, puncture into vertebral canal.

**Ren-** (L) *kidney:* adrenal, near the kidney.

**Retro-** (L) *backward:* retroversion, turned backward (usually, of uterus).

**Rhin-** (G) *nose:* rhinology, knowledge concerning noses.

**Salping-** (G) *a tube:* salpingitis, inflammation of tube.

**Semi-** (L) *half:* semicoma, mild coma.

**Septic-** (L and G) *poison:* septicemia, poisoned condition of blood.

**Somat-** (G) *body:* psychosomatic, having bodily symptoms of mental origin.

**Sta-** (G) *make stand:* stasis, stoppage of flow of fluid.

**Sten-** (G) *narrow:* stenosis, narrowing of duct or canal.

**Sub-** (L) *under:* subdiaphragmatic, under the diaphragm.

**Super-** (L) *above, excessively:* superacute, excessively acute.

**Supra-** (L) *above, upon:* suprarenal, above or upon the kidney.

**Sym-** or **Syn-** (G) *with, together:* symphysis, a growing together.

**Tachy-** (G) *fast:* tachycardia, fast-beating heart.
**Tens-** (L) *stretch:* extensor, a muscle extending or stretching a limb.
**Therm-** (G) *heat:* diathermy, therapeutic production of heat in tissues.
**Tox-** or **Toxic-** (G) *poison:* toxemia, poisoned condition of blood.
**Trache-** (G) *trachea:* tracheitis, inflammation of the trachea.
**Trans-** (L) *across:* transplant, transfer tissue from one place to another.
**Tri-** (L and G) *three:* trigastric, having three bellies (muscle).
**Trich-** (G) *hair:* trichosis, any disease of the hair.

**Uni-** (L) *one:* unilateral, affecting one side.

**Vas-** (L) *vessel:* vasoconstrictor, nerve or drug that narrows blood vessel.

**Zoo-** (G) *animal:* zooblast, an animal cell.

## Suffixes

**-algia** (G) *pain:* cardialgia, pain in the heart.
**-asis** or **-osis** (G) *affected with:* leukocytosis, excess number of leukocytes.
**-asthenia** (G) *weakness:* neurasthenia, nervous weakness.
**-blast** (G) *germ:* myeloblast, bone-marrow cell.
**-cele** (G) *tumor, hernia:* enterocele, any hernia of intestine.
**-cid** (L) *cut, kill:* germicidal, destructive to germs.
**-clysis** (G) *injection:* hypodermoclysis, injection under the skin.
**-coccus** (G) *round bacterium:* pneumococcus, bacterium of pneumonia.
**-cyte** (G) *cell:* leukocyte, white cell.
**-ectasis** (G) *dilation, stretching:* angiectasis, dilatation of a blood vessel.
**-ectomy** (G) *excision:* adenectomy, excision of adenoids.
**-emia** (G) *blood:* glycemia, sugar in blood.
**-esthesia** (G) (*noun*) *relating to sensation:* anesthesia, absence of feeling.

**-ferent** (L) *bear, carry:* efferent, carry out to periphery.
**-genic** (G) *producing:* pyogenic, producing pus.
**-iatrics** (G) *pertaining to a physician or the practice of healing* (medicine): pediatrics, science of medicine for children.
**-itis** (G) *inflammation:* tonsillitis, inflammation of tonsils.
**-logy** (G) *science of:* pathology, science of disease.
**-lysis** (G) *losing, flowing, dissolution:* autolysis, dissolution of tissue cells.
**-malacia** (G) *softening:* osteomalacia, softening of bone.
**-oma** (G) *tumor:* myoma, tumor made up of muscle elements.
**-osis (-asis)** (G) *being affected with:* atherosis, arteriosclerosis.
**-(o)stomy** (G) *creation of an opening:* gastrostomy, creation of an artificial gastric fistula.
**-o(tomy)** (G) *cutting into:* laparotomy, surgical incision into abdomen.
**-pathy** (G) *disease:* myopathy, disease of a muscle.
**-penia** (G) *lack of:* leukopenia, lack of white blood cells.
**-pexy** (G) *to fix:* proctopexy, fixation of rectum by suture.
**-phagia** (G) *eating:* polyphagia, excessive eating.
**-phasia** (G) *speech:* aphasia, loss of power of speech.
**-phobia** (G) *fear:* hydrophobia, fear of water.
**-plasty** (G) *molding:* gastroplasty, molding or re-forming stomach.
**-pnea** (G) *air or breathing:* dyspnea, difficult breathing.
**-poiesis** (G) *making, forming:* hematopoiesis, forming blood.
**-ptosis** (G) *falling:* enteroptosis, falling of intestine.
**-rhythmia** (G) *rhythm:* arrhythmia, variation from normal rhythm of heart.
**-rrhagia** (G) *flowing or bursting forth:* otorrhagia, hemorrhage from ear.
**-rrhaphy** (G) *suture of:* enterorrhaphy, act of sewing up gap in intestine.
**-rrhea** (G) *discharge:* otorrhea, discharge from ear.
**-sthen (ia) (ic)** (G) *pertaining to strength:* asthenia, loss of strength.
**-taxia** or **-taxis** (G) *order, arrangement of:* ataxia, failure of muscular co-ordination.
**-trophia** or **-trophy** (G) *nourishment:* atrophy, wasting, or diminution.
**-uria** (G) *to do with urine:* polyuria, excessive secretion of urine.